I Will Not Serve

Serve

The priest who said NO to Hitler

Based on the true story of Franz Reinisch

David Rice

RED STAG
MENTOR

Published in 2018 by:
RED STAG
(a Mentor Books imprint)
Mentor Books Ltd
43 Furze Road
Sandyford Industrial Estate
Dublin 18
Republic of Ireland

Tel: + 353 1 295 2112 / 3
Fax: + 353 1 295 2114
Email: admin@mentorbooks.ie
Website: www.mentorbooks.ie

A CIP catalogue record for this title is available from the British Library.

ISBN 978-1-912514-04-5

Cover Design: Kathryn O'Sullivan
Cover Image: Bridgeman Images

Edited by: Isobel Creed
                     Joan Lonergan

Visit our website: www.mentorbooks.ie

For Catherine Thorne

(Kathleen to me)

my companion

in all things

By the same author

Fiction

Blood Guilt
The Pompeii Syndrome
La Sindrome di Pompei
Song of Tiananmen Square

Non–fiction

Shattered Vows
The Dragon's Brood
Kirche ohne Priester
The Rathmines Stylebook

In preparation

Corduroy Boy
The Joy of Looking
The Book for the Bully
KHS Writing Guides 1-5
The Little Roads of Ireland

About the author

A NATIVE of Northern Ireland, David Rice has worked as a journalist on three continents. He has also been a Dominican friar. In the 1970s he was an editor and Sigma-Delta-Chi award-winning syndicated columnist in the United States, returning to Ireland in 1980 to head the prestigious Rathmines School of Journalism (later DIT). In 1989 he was invited to Beijing by the Thomson Foundation to train journalists on behalf of *Xin Hua*, the Chinese government news agency, and to work as an editor with China Features. He was in Beijing during the massacre of Tiananmen Square, and later returned to interview secretly 400 of the young people who had survived the massacre. This brought him to the attention of the Chinese security police. It also led to two books, *Dragon's Brood: Conversations with Young Chinese* (HarperCollins), and the novel, *Song of Tiananmen Square* (Brandon/Mt Eagle). His books have been published in Britain, Ireland, Germany, Italy and the United States. Rice's No.1 best-selling *Shattered Vows* (Michael Joseph/Penguin) led to the acclaimed Channel 4 documentary, *Priests of Passion*, which he presented. Educated at Clongowes, Rice has degrees in both Sociology and German Language & Literature from the National University of Ireland; in Community Development from Southern Illinois University, Carbondale, USA; and in Theology from the Angelicum University, Rome. He now lives in Co Tipperary, has taught Writing Skills at the University of Limerick, and has directed the Killaloe Hedge-School of Writing *(www.killaloe.ie/khs)*.

Acknowledgements

FIRST of all I am deeply indebted to the Schönstatt community in Vallendar-on-the-Rhine and the German Pallottine Fathers of the Berg-Sion-Regiohaus. I was their guest while researching the story of their confrère Franz Reinisch. It was there I walked the grounds where Reinisch walked in his agony of decision, and where I regularly visited the little chapel where he prayed for guidance, and the grave beside it where his ashes lie. I am also grateful to Ursula Kowalski, of the P. Reinisch-Sekretariat, who filled me in on so many details and gave me a great deal of available documentation – without exception in German, which I then had to translate. I especially thank Angela Marlier, of the *Presse- und Öffentlichkeitsarbeit* of the Franz Reinisch Forum for her painstaking scrutiny and advice on the text. The function of the Secretariat is to promote the cause for beatification and canonization of Franz Reinisch, and one hopes that this book will make that cause known more widely throughout the English-speaking world. I also must thank Dr Heinz-Jürgen Vogels who scrutinised the text of *I Will Not Serve* and guided me towards accuracy in many matters. I am grateful too to Dr Edgar Nawroth, of the German Dominican Fathers, who served as a priest in the *Wehrmacht* during World War Two, and enlightened me on many details about it. Thanks too to Isobel Creed of the Writers' Consultancy who edited the text; to Marjorie Quarton for her valuable comments; to my partner Catherine Thorne who guided me through many years of struggle to bring this story to light; to Joan Lonergan, her of the eagle eye for errors; and to Professor Marie Parker-Jenkins of the University of Limerick; to Eugene McDonough, my IT guru; to Danny McCarthy, my publisher, whose belief in this book has made all the difference; and the members of the Killaloe Writers' Group who put up with all my readings from the text which you now have in your hands.

~ DR

Author's note

THE 'New Journalism', pioneered by Gay Talese, Truman Capote, Tom Wolfe and others, is hardly new by now, but certainly still valid. Essentially it involves *telling a true story, but using a fictional format.* This means – among other things – creating scenes almost as in a movie, so the reader can see and hear things happen, rather than just being told what happens. It also means the creation of realistic dialogue that moves the story on, dialogue that might or might not have taken place. Even if it had, it might not possibly have been recorded or overheard unless one had been a fly on the wall. However sometimes a diary or a memoir can recall at least something of a conversation. There can occasionally be the introduction of a couple of fictional walk-on characters for the main character to interact with, allowing him to express his views. It involves, too, seeing what's happening from the main character's viewpoint. It can also involve giving the reader access to the thoughts inside that character's mind – the 'stream of consciousness' or 'interior monologue' beloved of Marcel Proust and James Joyce. And finally there is the depicting of the manners, customs and ambiance of the people of the time and place, so as to make the story come alive. *I WILL NOT SERVE* may well be the last true story to come out of Nazi Germany. I believe it needs to be told and that this is the best way to make it accessible to readers. One thing is for sure – *what we actually know about Franz Reinisch, and his stand against Adolf Hitler, is all here on these pages.* Almost all of my sources on Reinisch himself were written in German – first of all, his own prison diary, and principally works by Klaus Brantzen, Martin Emge, Klaus Hagmann, Heinrich Kreutzberg, Engelbert Monnerjahn, Heribert Niederschlag, Christian Feldmann and Wojciech Kordas. I have drawn freely on these, and they are listed at the end of the text. I have had to translate almost all of them before writing this book. It has taken years, but it has been worth it. I have also visited many of the places associated with Franz Reinisch, including the grave at Schönstatt where his ashes are buried, and have talked with various individuals who knew people who remembered him. No one who actually knew him could still be alive, as far as I can ascertain. I would be glad to be corrected on this.

~ David Stokes Rice

I liberate man from the constraint of a spirit... from the filthy and degrading torments inflicted on himself by a chimera called conscience and morality

~ Adolf Hitler

1

*Must the citizen even for a moment, or in the least degree, resigns his
conscience to the legislator? Why has every man a conscience then?
I think that we should be men first, and subjects afterward*

Henry David Thoreau

BAD KISSINGEN, Bavaria, Germany. Wednesday, 15 April, 1942. A bell clangs, the red tram moans away from the stop outside Manteuffel Barracks, and clatters off down windswept Nordring Street. Left standing at the tram stop in the gusting rain is a tall man in a long dark overcoat and wide-brimmed flat hat, a small brown suitcase in his left hand.

The man crosses the street to the roofed gate of the barracks, and presents a green envelope at the guard hut. He passes the white-and-red barrier as he is waved through. He hesitates, roots in his coat pocket, pulls out three packets of cigarettes, returns to the guard hut and hands them to the astonished but grateful occupant.

He walks slowly across the drenched tarmac towards the grim, square, central building with the green-capped clock

9

tower. The clock reads 2.48 p.m. The man stops to let a squad of helmeted youngsters thunder past on the double, urged on by a snarling NCO. Then he heads for the great triple doors of the barrack entrance.

Adolf Hitler gazes sternly across the entrance hall beyond the doors, from out of a two-metre-high framed picture. The hall smells of sweat, boot leather and carbolic. At the desk below Hitler, a grey-haired, grey-faced sergeant is reading a newspaper, one foot up on a chair.

'My call-up papers,' the man says. The sergeant holds out his hand without looking up, and takes the proffered envelope. He opens it, takes out the folded sheet and glances through it. Something there makes him look up.

'You a padre, then?'

'I am.'

Only then does the sergeant notice the white clerical collar atop the dripping raincoat. He grunts and glances further down the page. He taps it as he looks up again: 'According to this, you should have been here yesterday. Twenty-four hours late reporting for duty. I have to say, padre, you don't seem to place too much value on becoming a soldier.'

'I'd place a lot more value on it,' the tall man says, 'if I were going to be serving a different regime.'

A chill wind seems to have entered the bleak, boot-battered hall. The sergeant himself shivers: 'I – don't – think – I – heard – that,' he says.

'It's a lot worse than that, Sergeant,' the man says. 'I've come here to refuse military service. I'm not going to take the oath.'

10

'You're *WHAT?*'

'Let me say it again, sergeant. And listen carefully this time. *I am refusing military service.* I will not be swearing the *Fahneneid.*' [1]

Time stands still. The room is a tableau, with the sergeant gaping up at the dark figure towering silently above him.

Time moves again. The elderly sergeant twirls a handle and leans down to a phone on his desk, lifting the speaker to his ear. He speaks briefly, listens. Obviously no answer. A muttered curse, and the sergeant stands up. He grabs his cap and comes out from behind the desk. 'Don't you move,' he says to the man, and turns towards the corridor on the right. He hesitates, glances at the main doors and lifts a large bunch of keys from the desk.

'No need for that,' the man says. 'I'm not going anywhere.'

The sergeant hesitates again, shrugs, clips the keys to his belt, and limps slowly down the corridor into the maw of the barracks.

The lieutenant who strides into the hall is straight out of Leni Riefenstahl's *Triumph of the Will* – glinting jackboots, clipped blond hair, Aryan face sculpted by arrogance. With a click of his fingers he sends the sergeant back behind his desk and turns to the man in black, who towers over him by at least four inches. 'Name?'

'Reinisch. Franz Reinisch.'

'*Beruf?*'

'Roman Catholic priest.'

---

[1] The military oath of loyalty to Adolf Hitler (literally, 'Flag Oath')

'So what's this I'm told? The sergeant can't have got it right.'

'He got it right, all right. I am here to declare that I am refusing military service. I will not take the oath to Hitler. How many more times do I have to say it?'

'Are you out of your mind? It's the firing squad for even thinking this. That alone is treason.'

The word treason sends a shiver through all three men. There is silence for a moment.

'This is beyond my competence,' the lieutenant says. 'It's one for the Colonel. Meanwhile I'm placing you under arrest. Sergeant! Get this fellow into uniform and take him to the guardroom.'

'There'd be no uniform to fit him, Herr Leutnant. Look at the size of him.'

'Then *find* one. Send out for one. Do you hear me?' The jackboots clack off down the corridor.

2

Conscience is the perfect interpreter of life
Karl Barth

FELDKIRCH, Vorarlberg, Austria. 1 February, 1903. 3.50 a.m. There was a gasp of joy from the midwife when the newborn baby started to breathe. It had been a long struggle to get the inert little bundle to show any sign of life.

Dr Batliner, urgently summoned, had shaken his head several times. Now he shook his head in wonder: 'Something great will come of you, young fellow,' he said.

Ten years later the young fellow's utterly frustrated headmaster said, 'This boy will amount to nothing. He'll be a great cross to his parents.'

All of which suggests that Franz Reinisch was a figure of contradiction right from the start.

So too was his family, down through the generations. The folk of the Tyrol are not exactly an easy lot, and down through the centuries have fought for their freedom many times. And the Reinisch family were always part of that fight.

The name can be traced back to a 15th-century farm in Pustertal, from which down the years came farmers, teachers, lawyers, organ builders – and freedom fighters. In 1603 Archduke Maximilian of Austria conferred a crest in perpetuity on a Reinisch family – two brothers and three sons, 'in recognition of special services'. The crest aptly includes a lion rampant.

'The Scythe' was the epithet of one Anton Reinisch, a smith who used his scythe ferociously in battle against the troops of Napoleon, until he himself died at bayonet point in the Battle of Spinges in South Tyrol. A memorial to him in his home town of Volders shows him brandishing his scythe. Another memorial, to Reinisch and his comrades, in the Hofkirche in Innsbruck, reads as follows:

In eternal memory
Of the brave defenders of this land who, in the battle
At Spinges, 2.4.1797,
Heroically fought for God, Kaiser and Fatherland

Young Franz Reinisch seems to have had this fighting blood too. That initial struggle to breathe suggests he had to fight for his life from the very start. Indeed all his life Franz Reinisch would have to fight against ill health.

The infant nearly died at six weeks old. Appendicitis at 14, ear operations at 25, ersepalis of the kidneys at 33, chronic bowel trouble throughout his life, with paralysis of the colon on three different occasions.

Yet who would have guessed it: Franz Reinisch grew into a powerful man, well over six feet tall, showing enormous energy, creativity and leadership, with unflagging energy all his life.

And of course the fighting spirit was always there. Which was what had prompted the headmaster's observation that he'd come to nothing. There were too many scuffles with other schoolboys to be tolerated. Franz had a blazing temper when roused. His mother once caught the ten-year-old on top of a heap of stones, beating the daylights out of young Anton Loidl. Franz was not what mothers refer to as 'a nice boy'.

INNSBRUCK, 26 May, 1913. Youngsters Franz Reinisch and Anton Loidl stood on the Innstrasse sidewalk, watching gleefully as a tram rolled down the street. What would happen to the stone they'd put on the track? Would it be crushed to powder this time? Or maybe it would whizz through the air like a bullet, as it sometimes did. This was *fun*.

'Maybe it'll be derailed! Wouldn't that be great?' Franz rubbed his hands and chuckled. 'It's gotta happen sometime.'

A heavy hand descended on each shoulder. 'I saw what you little bastards did,' the policeman said. 'Wait till your parents hear about this. C'm'on. Let's go.'

When the policeman delivered the young law-breaker home, Mother Reinisch was distressed but not surprised. 'Leave him to me, officer,' she said. 'It won't happen again, I promise.'

The policeman hesitated, then touched his cap and left. These were people of consequence.

Mutti waited until the front door closed, and turned to her son. 'If your father gets to hear of this, you won't be able to sit for weeks. You know that, don't you?'

The kid nodded glumly, even though he didn't believe it. His papa didn't do walloping.

'Well, he won't hear about it from me – this time,' said the mother. 'But I want a promise – you will never, never do a thing like that again. Promise?'

Franz nodded again, this time relieved.

This was the same day that a 24-year-old fellow Austrian took the train from Vienna's Hüttendorf station bound for Munich. There he lodged with Josef Popp, and earned a meagre living as an artist. His name was Adolf Hitler.

Little Franz was a man of his word and he kept it: he never again put stones on the tramlines. Instead he began standing in front of trams and jumping away at the last moment. Of course it couldn't have continued, and finally the father got to hear about it.

There was the devil of a row.

After the confrontation, the father declared that from now on Master Franzl would be well behaved. One wonders what kind of a confrontation it must have been.

However there are no indications of an amended life. Indeed the elder brother Andreas many years later denied there had been any improvement, as did the two younger sisters.

It wasn't too long after this that Franz got an attack of diarrhoea on his way home from school, and made a dreadful mess of his shorts. What to do? He daren't go home like that.

16

What if some of the other kids saw him – he'd never live it down. So Franz climbed up on a wall and sat in the sun, waiting for his pants to dry.

There was worry at home when he didn't turn up, and the mother went looking for him. The kid was dying with embarrassment when she found him perched on the wall. But Mutti Reinisch was a kindly soul, reassured him, got him home and changed without anyone being the wiser. When she later told the Papa he just laughed gently. There'd be no confrontation over that.

The Reinisch parents were a kindly pair, but utterly demanding of their children in the things they considered important. Like being honest; telling the truth; following one's conscience; morning and night prayers; attendance at church; kindness to one another; caring for the less fortunate.

They were a handsome couple – she quiet, reserved, competent, with circular glasses and thick brown hair touched with grey; he tall and balding, mostly smiling, without the quick temper of his son, with the customary Kaiser-like waxed moustache, wing collar, watch and chain across the waistcoat, all as befitting a fairly high official in the Austrian Revenue Service.

Family life was a mixture of duties, work and play – especially music. Everyone played an instrument – the papa played the piano and violin; the mother the guitar. Franz played both piano and violin. The parents often sang together, and the children accompanied them on piano and violin. 'There was lots of laughter,' Franz's sister recalled years later. 'It was life and joy in our family.'

3

Conscience is what makes a boy tell his mother
before his sister does
Evan Esar

INNSBRUCK, Austria. 26 January, 1914. The ice beneath their feet was so slippery that it was hard to walk, as Franz and his papa headed into town.

'Come on Papa, why can't we take the tram?' the 11-year-old whined. He absolutely loved tram rides.

'All right, son. Just this once. But you know how walking is good for you.'

'Huh.' A snort through the nose.

There was a long wait, and the pair got colder and colder in the icy wind. Franz's fingers were starting to hurt inside the gloves, and his nose felt as if it would fall off.

What if I get frostbite, Franz was thinking, although this was highly unlikely. But he had read about it in Karl May's adventure novels. Nevertheless he'd risk the frostbite – he wanted to wait for that tram.

19

'How about we go to the next stop?' the papa suggested.

Franz didn't like this at all, as now there'd be less time on the tram. But he didn't have much option. So his temper was up when, halfway to the next stop, the tram came clanging past them.

At the next stop the papa said: 'Look, Franzl, it'll take too long if we wait here. If we run to the next stop, we'll be able to get on there.'

Franz burst into tears of fury.

'All right,' said the papa. 'Wait here if you want to. But I'm going ahead, whether you like it or not.'

Franz's temper had to cool. 'I suppose I'll have to come,' he grumped.

They set off at a run and got to the next stop in good time. The tram came rolling down the steep hill, skidded on the ice, came off the rails and crashed into a building just across from them. Shards of glass flew everywhere and there were screams from the wreck, as the two Reinischs ran across to help.

Just ten days later an Austrian draft board in Salzburg rejected a young man as 'unfit for military service – too weak. Incapable of bearing arms.' The young man's name was Adolf Hitler.

In the years following that tram crash, the family had a theory that this was the moment when Franz began to grow up and stop his nonsense. It took a considerable time, however.

SARAJEVO, Serbia. 28 June, 1914. 10.53 a.m. The young son of the Princips, a Bosnian family, who had been named Gavrilo in honour of the Angel Gabriel, stood outside Schiller's

Delicatessen across from the ancient Latin Bridge. The morning sun was warm on his bare arms, the air had that fresh morning tang, and the Miljacka River sparkled in the sunlight. Gavrilo was awaiting the passing of Archduke Franz Ferdinand of Austria, heir presumptive to the Austro-Hungarian throne.

But he was not waiting to cheer. When the 1911 Gräf & Stift open-topped car turned off the Appel Quay, it halted and backed to change direction. The engine stalled. Gavrilo Princip stepped forward, raised his 9×17mm Fabrique Nationale semi-automatic pistol, and fired two shots.

The first bullet slashed into the Archduke's jugular vein; the second buried itself in the abdomen of the Duchess, his wife. Both died shortly after. The Archduke's last words were, 'Sophie, Sophie, don't die. Live for our children!'

The gunshots echoed throughout Europe, and were then followed by a terrible silence. On 1 August Austria broke that silence, issuing an ultimatum to Serbia, and World War One broke out.

Three days later the King of Bavaria received a petition from a young man, begging to be allowed to serve in the German military in spite of being an Austrian citizen. The petition was granted. Adolf Hitler later called it 'the greatest and most unforgettable time of my earthly existence'.

Papa Reinisch received his call-up papers two weeks after the outbreak of war. When he went to the military barracks to register, both Franz and his brother Andreas went along with him to give him moral support. They had to wait more than two hours, until a very relieved papa came out brandishing a

21

paper. It was a temporary postponement of military service, giving the reason that he was indispensable in his Revenue work. He was never recalled to service.

HALL, Tyrol, Austria. 11 September, 1914. The mountains were already blazing with snow around this lovely town, when Franz and Andreas arrived at the Leopoldinum, the Franciscan school here.

Franz had been as cross as two sticks when he learned of his papa's decision: 'Why do we have to be boarders?' he grumped. 'Sure it's only 10 km from Innsbruck. We could take the bus every day.'

But Papa was adamant. 'A bit more discipline will do you no harm, young fellow. There'll be no jumping in front of trams here.'

'But I haven't done that for months, Papa. You know that. That's a rotten thing to say.'

'I know you haven't, son. And that wasn't fair of me. But give it a chance: you'll really learn so much here, and there'll be no distractions. And you can come home at weekends anyhow. You'll give it a try, won't you?'

'Huh!' One of those snorts.

However both young fellows quickly got to enjoy their stay at the school. The beauty of the mountains and the River Inn tumbling through them, and the frequent hikes into the foothills, soon won Franz over. The Franciscans ran a strict but fair regime, and there were some gifted teachers among them. Franz's school work improved noticeably.

There was one priest who particularly impressed Franz. Father Anthony took the boys hiking, to visit the Mint Museum and the Mint Tower where all the coins had been made. But when he took Franz to Wahlpachgasse to see the paintings by Christopher Anton Mayr of the life of Saint Francis, something began to stir in young Franz Reinisch.

During the months that followed, Father Anthony told him about their founder, and of Francis's love for birds and all God's creatures, and how he had given everything away to become a poor man. And how that was the ideal of the Franciscans to this very day.

Franz was just starting to think that maybe this was the way his life might go, when suddenly Father Anthony was no longer there. Word came that he had been transferred to Bozen [Bolzano], and Franz never again heard of him, or from him.

Years later Franz mentioned that he might have become a Franciscan if there had been more time with Father Anthony. As it was, thoughts of a vocation quietly faded.

HALL, Tyrol, Austria. 1919. Other thoughts began to take the place of such pious notions. Thoughts of girls, in particular. These thoughts were facilitated after the brothers had persuaded Papa to allow a move into lodgings in downtown Hall, when they were starting their sixth year at the school.

Franz, who was now 16, relished this newfound freedom. It was at this time that he tried his first cigarette.

'Go on, suck it right in,' fellow student Kurt Schuschnigg urged him. 'Right down to the bottom of your lungs. There's nothing quite like it.'

There certainly wasn't, especially when Franz started coughing his heart out and ended up throwing up.

'You'll get used to it,' was Kurt's grinning comment.

But Franz was a man who persevered, and soon was smoking his head off. That first cigarette after breakfast was the loveliest of all, when the smoke did indeed go right to the bottom of the lungs. There was no feeling quite like it. Older brother Andreas disapproved, but he had by then become what Franz considered a studious old grump, always at his maths books.

Franz of course went his own way, and joined the Sterncorona student association. It was there he encountered the wonderful world of women.

And he encountered it again when the boys returned to live with their family in Innsbruck. Many times. His outward appearance improved as his studies declined.

'I'm not ironing your trousers again,' younger sister Hanni yelled at Franz. 'That's three times this week. You're a conceited idiot – prancing up and down Maria Theresa Street and showing off to the girls. You'd be better off taking a job like Andreas. Instead of scrounging off him to pay for those cigarettes. D'y'hear?'

'You watch that tongue of yours, Hanni!'

'No use losing your temper, big brother. I'm not one of your dumb dolls out there. Just cool down, and go out and get a job. And iron your own blooming trousers!'

Franz took a job behind the bar of the Leopoldina. He lasted three weeks.

24

The end of the war brought considerable changes. There was a scarcity of food and firewood, and relics of the war were everywhere, even though this was an unoccupied zone.

'Come here and see what I've found,' Franz whispered to Andreas in the room they shared. He shook the sack in his hand and a revolver and a bayonet clattered to the floor.

'God, where did you find those?'

'In the school. Behind a shutter in the basement. Those billeted soldiers must've left them. The gun's still loaded. Nobody else knows.'

Andreas lifted the bayonet by its blade. 'You can't keep this. I'm going straight to Papa with it.'

'You will not. Give it to me!'

In the struggle that followed, Franz pulled the bayonet away, cutting four fingers of his brother's right hand. That took a bit of explaining, but Andreas gave some lame excuse. He wasn't going to snitch on his brother. He didn't dare.

Franz headed out with the loaded revolver. He went to the nearby woods to practise shooting at trees. One shot went wide and smashed through a window of the nearby convent. Rumour had it that it just missed the Reverend Mother's nose.

In the subsequent uproar, neither pistol nor perpetrator was ever found.

In times of scarcity the concepts of mine and thine can get easily confused. One day the two brothers arrived to their family home and presented their mother with a few kilos of coffee and sugar, which had 'fallen off a lorry'. Their mother gratefully accepted the gifts.

25

Their father did not. Nor was he grateful. 'Come up to my study,' he said to the boys, after he came home and learned about the acquisitions. This was serious, the boys realised. More serious than just sugar or coffee. That study, smelling of cedar cigar boxes and leather chairs, was where important things were discussed.

'I don't want to know where all this came from,' Papa began. 'But it goes right back there. Immediately. Is that clear?'

Andreas hung his head glumly. Franz was more defensive: 'But it's only a couple of kilos, Papa.'

'That's not the point, Franzl. It's the little things that matter. That's what conscience is about – not whether a thing is big or small, but whether it's right or wrong. Nothing to do with size. Remember what the catechism says, "He that contemneth small things shall fall by little and little."

'I'll make you a promise, Franzl. I'll make it to both of you. If you stick by your conscience, always, in absolutely everything, even the tiniest things, you'll never go wrong in the big things. You'll suffer of course, at times, but always remember, an easy conscience is a soft cushion. Never forget it.'

4

Conscience is the voice of the soul;
the passions, of the body
Rousseau

INNSBRUCK, Austria. 28 September, 1922. *Immobiles sicut patriae montes* – 'As Immovable as the Hills of Home'. That was the motto of the Leopoldina – the student fraternity that Franz Reinisch immediately joined when he entered the Law Faculty at Innsbruck University. It was a motto which, along with his father's advice about conscience, seemed to him in later life to have been crucial.

But not quite yet. Life changes when you move to third level. It certainly did for Franz. The exams were a year away, and it was a time of singing, festivals, pubs and dancing. The fraternity was his focus. So much so that Mother Reinisch told himself and Andreas they'd better make their beds at the fraternity if they kept coming home so late.

'Do you have any idea how popular you are?' a wide-eyed girl said to Franz in the student bar. 'They're all mad about you here. And you don't even know it, do you?'

Franz knew it very well indeed. It's a heady thing to find oneself suddenly popular, and Franz revelled in it. He was six feet five inches tall, with Nordic good looks, a brilliant dancer, and a gifted player of both piano and cards. It would be hard not to enjoy it all. The cut of his jackets became the very latest, though mostly they were second hand. Even the cigarettes changed – it was nice to be able to slap down a packet of *Heer & Flotte* [2] on the bar table.

It took his younger sister once more to take him down to size. 'Know something, Franzl – you've changed,' she told him one day. 'And we don't like the new you. You're so blooming conceited, you'd think you were God almighty's second cousin. Just you wait, and you'll get your come-uppance.'

'That's jolly unfair, Hanni. Give us a break, will you! I'm the same Franzl as always.'

'You're not, y'know. Who else comes home three times a day to change his clothes? Who still makes his sisters iron his pants? Who's always swanning around in his fraternity robes? Who spends hours at the mirror brushing his hair and doing his nails and admiring himself? Know something – I wouldn't be surprised they're all laughing at you behind your back!'

Franz exploded in rage, tried to splutter an answer but couldn't think of one, so he stormed out of the house, slamming the front door behind him.

A couple of hours later he was back in the house, climbing the stairs a bit sheepishly. At the top he encountered his sister and gave her a big hug. 'I'm sorry Hanni,' he whispered. 'Tell me, you didn't mean all that, did you?'

---

[2] *Army & Navy* – name of a popular cigarette brand

'Not about the laughing,' she said.

INNSBRUCK, Austria. 9 December, 1922. Edith Costa looked like a doll beside 19-year-old Franz Reinisch. At least that's how it looked to older brother Andreas, when he spotted them emerging arm-in-arm from the Botanic Gardens into Sternwartestrasse. But as they came closer Andreas could see she was far from doll-like – a fine, strapping, 18-year-old in a dirndl, with long blond plaits. She was however still two heads shorter than Franz, and she was looking up at him with something like adoration.

Franz's face tightened as the pair came up to Andreas. He shook his head slightly, gave a slight wink, and passed by without a greeting. The message was clear: Andreas was to mind his own business, and also to keep his mouth shut.

He did neither.

Papa Reinisch was not pleased, to say the least, when Andreas spilled the beans. 'I wish to speak to you later,' he said to Franz. 'Come up to my study after dinner.'

And Franz was furious with his snitcher brother. 'You *verdammtes Arschloch,*' he roared at him. 'It was none of your bloody business. Why'd you have to spoil things, like you always do? Know what's wrong with you, Andreas? I'll tell you what – you're just jealous because you don't have a girl. And you know why? Because no girl would look at you – that's why!'

'Easy on, little brother. You need to watch that temper of yours. It'll get you into trouble, sooner or later.' Andreas spoke cheerfully, but it was clear he was deeply hurt. There was a sort of fixed smile on his face as he walked past his sister and down the stairs to the street.

'Well, I hope you're proud of yourself, you nasty little bastard,' Hanni said to her brother. 'You've really made his day. Andreas will be a while getting over this one.'

Ten minutes later Franz was no longer furious with his brother. But he was with himself. Andreas is right: these eruptions could get me into trouble. They've just done it: I've hurt Andreas something awful, and I can't take back the words. That's the trouble – you can't unsay things. O dear God, help me with this temper of mine. It could destroy people. Me included.

Andreas accepted the proffered apology later that day. But it was clear that the words had cut deep.

Franz Reinisch always associated the leather and cigar-box smell of his father's study with matters serious.

'Do you realise that the Costas aren't even Catholic?' The leather chair creaked as Papa Reinisch leaned back. 'There are lots of lovely girls out there, in the Leopoldina – why do you have to go and pick a Lutheran? I mean, you can hardly marry one, can you?'

'I can't help it, Papa. I have such strong feelings for her.'

'Look. Son, we've all had feelings like that. I had lots of them before I married your Mother. But we get over them. Just give it time. *You'll* get over it too.'

'I've no intention of getting over it, Papa. I love her. She's a good, clean, honest girl, and a lot better than some of the

Catholic girls in the Leopoldina.' Franz steeled himself for the next utterance. 'I'm actually thinking of marrying her, Lutheran or not.'

Papa did not explode in wrath, as his son might have done in similar circumstances. Instead, the two men sat in silence for some moments.

Papa took off his pince-nez and occupied himself with polishing them. Then he sighed. 'Do as you like, Franz – you're a grown man now. But can I give you a bit of advice? First *become* something – whatever it is you want to be. An advocate, a doctor, a civil servant like myself. And then you will have something to offer a girl. Right now, what are you? A penniless student. What could you offer this woman? The life of a student? Please, my boy. Just wait a while.'

Franz did wait, but not for very long. Edith Costa's family moved to Vienna shortly afterwards. There were letters between them for a while, but they gradually became fewer, as letters sometimes do. Absence does not always make the heart grow fonder.

By then Franz had found Ludowika Linhard. This graceful, athletic young woman, skier in winter and hiking companion in summer, seemed to carry with her, wherever she went, a breath of the outdoors. Only trouble was, she too was Lutheran. In those pre-ecumenical days this was a real problem, but it did not deter Franz in the least. And Papa Reinisch had by now learnt to keep his thoughts to himself. At least where his younger son was concerned.

The study of law can be
a nation arguing with its conscience
Barack Obama

INNSBRUCK, Austria. February 2, 1923. Kurt Schuschnigg could be persuasive. This friend from schooldays, who had given Franz his first cigarette, was now a young lawyer, heading for a promising political career. He and his Herma spent a lot of time with Franz and Ludowika, who were by now head-over-heels in love. Together they were regarded in Innsbruck as a kind of foursome.

The four of them were looking out over the Stubai Glacier from a restaurant table in the Grünwalderhof. The setting winter sun seemed to cast a gentle warmth over the glacier. The after-dinner *doppeltgebrannter* schnapps was bringing a gentle warmth to the temples of Franz Reinisch.

'There's this retreat in Wyhlen,' Kurt was saying to Franz. 'It's that 30-days thing the Jesuits do. This one's for academics. Would you be interested? It'd cost you nothing.'

'*You're* going, I take it?'

Kurt chuckled. 'I've better things to do right now.' He put an arm around Herma. 'We've just got engaged!'

Mouths opened, and Franz raised a congratulatory fist in the air. 'Well I declare. Well done, Kurt. Congrats. And Herma, years of happiness to you.' He raised his glass.

There was a pause. 'Could Ludowika come? To the retreat, I mean.'

'I hardly think so. I mean, she's a Protestant, isn't she?'

'That's it, then. You can forget it. I'm going nowhere without Ludowika.'

Ludowika's hand tightened on his.

'Think it over, anyhow, my friend,' Kurt said. 'You might change your mind.'

WYHLEN, Baden-Württemberg, Germany. 28 February, 1923. Franz Reinisch was lonely in this lovely place. In the foothills of the Black Forest, with a stunning view of the Swiss Alps, the retreat house should have been a place of peace. But not when you've left behind the love of your life, and are facing 30 days in solitary. Franz was miserable. *Why did I ever listen to that bloody Schuschnigg?*

But whatever it was that brought it about, something gradually began to happen in the spirit of Franz Reinisch.

At first it was the sheer, utter loneliness. Franz had hardly known the meaning of loneliness, and when you've never been lonely you don't really bother to do much thinking, or have time to. Now there was time, buckets of it.

As the great Saxon warrior Elmar says, in FW Weber's *Dreizehnlinden* --

34

Loneliness nourishes the soul

In stillness there comes to the soul

True disclosure

And somehow the loneliness began to nourish the soul of this man who had hardly been lonely before in his life. There was time to think, perhaps for the first time ever.

Loneliness in a lovely place is different from the harsh loneliness in a city. The word *Waldeinsamkeit* is dear to the Germanic soul – the loneliness of the forest. And this retreat house was right on the edge of the trees, separated only by a tumbling little stream. Franz walked day after day among those trees, and, even bare in winter, the trees began to work their magic.

The things Franz thought about, however, began gradually to change. Inspiration came from an unusual man, Father Martin Graf Dunin-Borkowski SJ. This Austrian nobleman has been described by philosopher Josef Pieper as 'one of the very few people known to me to whom I would unhesitatingly attribute wisdom'.

As retreat master, Borkowski began to lead Franz gently, first via lectures and then through personal counselling.

'The key to everything,' he explained to him one afternoon during that first week, 'is the conquest of oneself. Look at those brown-stained fingers – what do they tell you? That cigarette you're smoking right now: do you think you could ever conquer that attachment?'

Franz hesitated, then stubbed the cigarette out on the ashtray which the priest genially held out. For an instant he wanted to hit him.

'A tiny first step,' smiled the priest. 'But remember, this is not about will power. It's about the strength that comes your way if you ask for the grace. And that comes from God's love, which will free you from all these attachments. In fact everything we do here is about freedom. But real freedom.'

From then on Franz smoked only in the woods. But he made progress in a few other things. Above all he learned about discernment. He learned about the two drives in the human soul – the one towards goodness, and the other towards evil, and how hard it sometimes is to distinguish between the two. The drive to evil can often look so reasonable. At times only God's gift of discernment can show which is which – in other words, the gift of an enlightened conscience.

At the end of the 30 days Franz Reinisch was not too sure how much had changed in him, but he wrote out a couple of resolutions. The one that remained with him was – always to listen to the voice of God in my conscience.

There was no resolution about smoking.

KIEL, Schleswig-Holstein, Germany. 27 March, 1923. There was much to recommend this north-German port when Franz Reinisch arrived at the university here for a couple of semesters in Forensic Medicine. To begin with, the raging inflation meant his Austrian schillings went a great deal further. His digs off Blücherplatz cost a quarter of what he would have paid in Innsbruck.

It was less than five years since the sailors' mutiny in Kiel had led to the nationwide revolution that toppled the Kaiser, and the city, especially the port area, still retained a heady atmosphere of rebellion and independence. Franz's old Austrian charm still worked and he quickly made friends in the Rheno-Westphalia fraternity which his flat-mate Ralph King invited him to join.

The two were well matched – this hot-blooded Tyrolean and the laid-back Irishman from Cork. Even though King was older by ten years, people often took them for brothers – both tall, good-looking, one with the horn-rimmed glasses, which was Franz's distinguishing feature.

Fresh from Zurich after a stint at the Burghölzli under Eugen Bleuler, King was researching a doctorate on the distinct world outlook of seaport inhabitants, starting from their depiction in Wagner's *Der Fliegende Holländer*.

From his native city King was well aware of the attractions of a port, and the pair quickly discovered the waterfront bars. They also soon discovered that their student scarves and fraternity peaked caps were not altogether welcome among the sailors' caps of the harbour.

'No fucking *gleichgeschlectlich* in this place!' A huge figure in sailor's cap and striped vest loomed above the two men, as they sat one night outside the Nordsee Kneipe on the harbour quayside. The table trembled as the man's belly touched its edge.

Franz went to rise in anger but King's hand gently touched his arm. Two equally burly figures loomed behind Herr Stripes.

'You get the fuck out of here before you end up in the water,' Stripes growled. His breath was stifling as he reached across and deftly tipped over the stiefels of beer, one into either man's crotch. 'Out! Now! Run, you *verdammte* queers!'

For a man who changed clothes thrice a day, a stroll home trying to hide a wet crotch was as salutary a learning experience as any retreat.

They used to say about Father Borkowski that he never converted anybody. What he did was to sow seeds in a person's psyche – seeds that could take months or years to germinate. Perhaps that's what happened to Franz Reinisch during his two semesters in Kiel. However there were plenty of other experiences here that could change a man. All that forensic medicine stuff, for instance.

The faculty here at Kiel, working along with police and the law, believed in dropping its students in at the deep end of that pool of awfulness that is part of any maritime city. Severed heads and limbs; the stench of bodies dredged from the harbour; women ripped open from vagina to navel – Kiel had it and plenty more to offer.

Ralph King helped Franz to cope. His knowledge of psychology gently and gradually helped the younger man towards a balanced view of the peculiar thing that is human nature. The horrors of a harbour town, he explained, are just the dark side of the most absolutely urgent of all male human needs – the need for the Feminine. And if we don't somehow fulfil that need, we lose our way in life.

'You mean sex?'

'That's just one aspect of it – the drive to beget children. But it goes far, far deeper than that. This whole male patriarchal society is all about hunting, killing, controlling, fighting, and war. Yet there is a crying out for the other element – the caring and the loving. Believe it or not, the deepest drive of all is the longing for a mother. The ancient religions had it – with goddesses like Demeter and Astarte. Aphrodite. Even Venus.'

'Well, they're all a bit passé nowadays, surely. We've got nothing like that.'

'Curiously enough, we do.'

'We do?'

'Yeah. We've got Mary, the Mother of God.'

'Oh, come off it, Ralph.'

Back in Innsbruck it would have been possible in that era for a young man about town to remain a virgin, especially if he mixed with the young women of respectable families, whose price invariably was matrimony. Which is where Franz Reinisch had socialised. Kiel however was somewhat different. The ladies preening in shop windows; those mysterious creatures in doorways who asked if you were lonely, dear, could leave a young man wondering. Wondering what it might be like.

One night during *Kielerwoche*, the city's carnival week at the end of June, Franz was walking home along Holstenstrasse when one such lady enquired after his loneliness. She fell into step with him and he did not shoo her away. Her perfume touched his nostrils. It gently spoke of musk.

A quick sidelong glance showed that she was young. And rather pretty. Franz could feel his heart beginning to thump. His saliva increased. A pleasant lightness and warmth at the back of his skull spread downwards through his body. He couldn't quite speak.

They were now going through darker streets. At one corner the girl gently steered him down a side street, into that warren of alleyways around the port. Franz walked almost in a trance.

Under a street lamp they stopped and Franz turned to face the young woman. As he held her shoulders he was breathing hard, as if he had been running. There was an agonizing pause.

'You won't do,' Franz muttered. 'You've got a squint!' Which the poor girl hadn't. In that instant he took off, running. As he did so he glanced back and saw the dark figures of two men moving up to the girl, who pointed in his direction.

He was now running for his life, and did not stop until he reached his digs.

Franz and Ralph King talked until four that morning. 'I'm glad you ran,' King said. 'You won't regret it.'

'How do you know?'

'I've done it,' King said.

'Ran?'

'No. *Stayed!*'

'Whores?'

'The lot – when I was your age. You name it. Whores, students, nice kids, all sorts. Even a fellow's wife, God forgive me. Cork was a bloody great place to start. Trouble is, it got serious there.'

'How serious?'

'You wouldn't want to know. So serious that – well – oh, forget it!'

'Go on!'

'No, I won't. Just don't ask.'

'Go on!'

'Did you hear what I said? Don't ask. Now will you back off!'

'Well, you've started now. You might as well go on.'

'I've never told anyone...'

'Maybe it's time you did.'

There was a long pause. King had his face in his hands. Franz lit another Heer & Flotte, and waited, saying nothing.

King looked up, and his eyes were moist. 'It's something I'll regret until the day I die.'

'Making love, you mean?'

' Aw, for Christ's sake grow up, will you. *No.* Not fucking, but fucking *up.* That's different. Getting things all wrong. Fucking's great when it's right, but Jeeesus, it's hell when it goes wrong. And I got it wrong. God, did I *what!*'

'What in God's name are you on about?'

King sighed. 'There was this lovely Cork lassie. Fiona. Drop-dead gorgeous she was. She got pregnant, and said I was the dad.'

'And were you?'

'Probably. No, pretty certain I was. But I said no, I wasn't. I said it could be one of the others. Well, that was just possible.

41

Just. Anyhow I'd my studies to finish and I just couldn't take it on. All I can say now is, may God forgive me.'

'It's hardly the end of the world.' Franz could think of nothing else to say.

'That's exactly what it is. The end of the world. For me. No, for *her*. She was fished out of Cork harbour, baby inside her.'

All Franz could hear was the tock, tock, tock of the clock.

'Oh, if I could put the clock back,' King murmured. 'But that's... Oh, let's not talk about it.'

'So what'll you do now?'

'Look, if I could just find forgiveness. The only way I can think of, is maybe bringing forgiveness to others. Or helping them to forgive themselves. In fact, that's what I've been trying to do for the last eight years, as a counsellor in a mental hospital. Lately I don't think it's enough. Priests do it better than us counsellors.'

'So what more can you do?'

'Well, I've got this crazy idea. When I get back to Ireland – you know, after I finish this damn doctorate – I'm thinking I might apply to one of those religious orders. One of the missionary crowds. Study to be a priest, you know. That's if they'd have me.'

'Would you tell them – about – ?'

'D'y'think I'm daft?'

6

INNSBRUCK, Austria. 14 July, 1923. Papa Reinisch was anything but enthusiastic about the proposal his younger son put to him. 'Son, I can't think of anyone less cut out to be a priest,' he said straight out. 'And your poor mother'd have a fit.'

'Why would she, Papa?'

'Look, Franzl. Have you any idea how impulsive you are? I mean – anyhow, what about Ludowika? You can't just walk out on her. Even if she is a Protestant.'

Franz sighed. 'Ja, she's the biggest problem, Papa. I wouldn't want to hurt her for worlds. I haven't got around to that yet. I just need time.'

Mother Reinisch didn't have a fit. 'Have you prayed about this, Franzl?' she asked.

43

'I've prayed, Mother, like I never did before in my life. Actually I never knew how, before. How to pray, I mean. But that Father Borkowski taught us things. Show me thy will, he told us to keep asking. That's the one prayer that's guaranteed an answer, he told us. And I've been saying it over and over since I got back from Kiel.'

'Well, Franzl, now I'm going to tell you something. Something I've never told anyone before in my life. Not even your Papa.'

Mother Reinisch put her hands together, leaned back and closed her eyes. 'When we were in Bozen, and you weren't yet six months old, I was watching the Corpus Christi procession – I was on the sidewalk with you in the pram. I can't remember where your Papa was. Anyhow, when the Monstrance came by, I took you out of the pram, and lifted you up. What I said was, "Dear Lord, if you will take this child to be a priest, I offer him to you with all my heart".'

She took her son's hand in hers. 'Franzl, I've carried this offer as a secret in my heart all these years. You see, I never wanted to push you into the priesthood, so I never told you. And even now I don't want to influence you. It could still be that it's not for you. Maybe God didn't accept my offer. Remember, his answer to prayer can sometimes be No. But I'll tell you this – from now on, I'll pray and sacrifice more and more for you. I'll pray that the right thing will come.'

Ludowika Linhard had no problems whatsoever with Franz's decision. 'He'll be back out in a month,' she said. 'That fellow'll never stick it!'

44

In fact there was no need to come back out from anywhere, for Franz didn't have to go away, even when he began to study for the priesthood. After enquiries had been made to the diocesan office, he was told simply to sign up with the university's theology faculty there in Innsbruck. And it wasn't even theology, but the first two years of scholastic philosophy.

One might conclude that they didn't have much hopes for a vocation for Franz Reinisch. Anyhow he was told to continue for the first two years as a lay student, but to undertake a lifestyle that would have him ready for celibacy when the time came.

Which is easier said than done. In fact it was daft. And indeed cruel to expect him to do that among all those lovely young women with whom he had hung around for years.

Ludowika Linhard was of course the biggest problem. At first she regarded it as just one more of those madcap notions that her Franzl got into his head from time to time. He'd been a bit peculiar since that time in Kiel, but he'd get over it. Some crazy Irishman had been putting notions into his head. He'd admitted as much.

It ended up in one unholy row.

'So you won't come to the dance?' Ludowika demanded. 'What's got into you?'

'You know perfectly well what's got into me. I've told you, I'm planning to become a priest.'

'But that's way down the line. You're a free man right now. What's to stop you coming?'

'Wika. It would be cruel to you. I mean, if I kept this relationship going, and then have to drop you when it's time.'

'You're going to drop me?'

'What else can I do? I mean, if I'm going to be a priest.'

'And who will you have in your life then? That Virgin Mary the priests go on about? That Thing up in the grotto with its plaster arms stretched out? Oh Franzl, look at *my* arms – they're stretched out too. But they're warm. They're real. They're opened for you. So are my legs, Franzl. I'm offering you a warm bed when the time comes, Franzl. Love, Franzl – warm love. Children to dandle on your knee. For you to love. To love you back. Grand-kids when we're both old. Descendants – maybe thousands in a thousand years' time. Franzl, I – love – you... Can't you understand?'

Tears forced their way between Franz's tightly-shut eyelids. 'Please, Wika. I can't take any more right now. It's too – too – please, Wika. Just leave me. Just go. I'm begging you.'

It was on 8 November of that year, 1923, that Franz espied Ludowika across Sternwartestrasse. She was arm-in-arm with that creep Stefan Goetschl.

Franz went home and wept. And wept until he could weep no more.

On that same evening, just 62 miles north of where Franz was weeping, a number of brown-shirted men were entering a crowded beer hall in Munich and lining up along the walls in a highly intimidating fashion. In the uproar that followed, a man fired a shot and this brought silence. The man stepped onto the stage and began to speak. 'It was a rhetorical masterpiece,' an

The Reinisch family in the 1930s. *Front*: Parents Franz Reinisch and Maria Reinisch née Huber
Rear from left: Andreas (older brother); Johanna ('Hanni'); Sr Agilberta Mariedl ('Marianne');
Fr Franz Reinisch, SAC (Pallotine); Martha Reinisch (teacher*)*.

Photo courtesy Franz Reinisch Forum, Schönstatt

onlooker later said. 'In a few short sentences he totally transformed the mood of the audience. I've rarely experienced anything like it.' The man's name was Adolf Hitler. The next day he was almost killed in an attempted coup, and later imprisoned for treason.

7

*Conscience is the internal perception of
the rejection of a particular wish
operating within us*
Sigmund Freud

BRIXEN-IM-THALE, Tyrol, Austria. 11 June, 1925. Franz Reinisch wore his black seminarian robes against a panorama of colour. The Eucharistic procession wound its way across a carpet of flowers through the cobbled streets and across the square to the church. Ahead of him walked altar servers in their red cassocks and white surplices; Tyrolean riflemen in their green chamois-plumed alpine hats, red waistcoats and brown *lederhosen*; Children of Mary all in blue; drummers in red and black; Carmelite nuns in beige; rows of little girls in first-communion white; women in green dirndl skirts and jauntily tilted *tracht* hats.

The scent of the rose petals rose in the June mountain air. The folks from three towns – Brixen, Kirchberg and Westendorf – lined the streets, kneeling as the Monstrance passed. The streets echoed to the lovely Austrian hymn, *Schönster Herr Jesu*:

> Fair are the meadows, fairer still the woodlands,
> Robed in the blooming garb of spring;
> Jesus is fairer, Jesus is purer,
> Who makes the woeful heart to sing.
> Fair is the sunshine, Fairer still the moonlight,
> And all the twinkling starry host;
> Jesus shines brighter, Jesus shines purer

This was more than a Corpus Christi procession – this was the *Antlassritt*, commemorating how the men from those towns had beaten back the Swedes in the Thirty Years' War, three hundred years earlier.

Franz's mind was miles away. He looked across at the Hohe Salve, still gleaming under its mantle of snow, and there came to him an image of Ludowika flipping her skis sideways as she finished her slalom run. Strangely enough, she was once again in his life, but in a very different way from before.

More than a year ago they had met unexpectedly, at the foundation day of the Leopoldina. When they nervously sat together over a beer, Franz was surprised to hear Ludowika say, 'Franz, I've thought and prayed, and I now believe you've made the right decision. And I pray every day that you will reach your goal.'

From then on, Ludowika became a sort of confidant, indeed a spiritual guide, and this continued when Franz entered the seminary at Brixen. Franz best described it in a letter to her from the seminary:

You must not take it badly, that I have been so taciturn... I can only say that through you I have step by step brought my vocation nearer. You have no idea how much support you have given me. Whether I wandered off, or got up to my tricks in Innsbruck, you were there for me in the hardest times – a wonderful figure who, with deep spirituality and a warning eye, often showed me the way to the Light.

Of course there were the times of despondency. Times even when it occurred to Franz that, if he became a Lutheran minister, he could both marry and have his priesthood. But such notions were in those days unthinkable and they were swiftly unthought.

His fellow seminarians could be irritating, and Franz had trouble with his quick temper. To a man of 22, who had experienced genuine love, as well as life in places like Kiel, some of these young fellows seemed like children. Nor did some of the professors impress him greatly. A few seemed never to have left the seminary, or at least never to have grown up, or certainly never to have experienced the things they lectured about.

An exception to all this was a Father Richard Weickgenannt. He was on loan from a religious order called the Pallottines, which Franz had never heard of. The close-cropped hair, with a hint of premature grey at the temples, and the way the man carried himself, almost suggested someone from the military. But there was a kindness there, and a gentleness that was often a healthy influence on Franz Reinisch.

'You've got to be patient with these young fellows, Franz,' he said, as the two of them were walking the seminary garden. 'They're only out of school. Were you much better at that age?'

'Well then, they shouldn't be here. They haven't the least notion of what celibacy's about – they haven't an idea of what they're undertaking. What'll happen when they meet a woman for the first time? Well, there's one or two that'll never bother with women. But the rest? God help them if they're ever ordained.'

The pair sat down at the little grotto, looking up at the Hohe Salve glinting beyond the trees.

'In a way you could be right.' Weickgenannt was thoughtful. 'Compared to our world, this place is like a nursery school. Sometimes I think the authorities are into cradle-snatching. And you know it's even worse in Italy – there they take them in at eleven. Can you imagine? I remember a seminary president in Reggio Emilia telling me it means they get a better understanding of priesthood. *Quatsch.* If you ask me, I'd question the validity of their ordination.'

'Anyhow, I suppose there's nothing we can do about it. I've my work cut out trying to survive, myself.'

'Don't we all! And there's one thing we've both forgotten, by the way, in all we've been talking about. The most important thing of all – for those youngsters and for us. We have to leave room for God's grace.'

It seems that, even though he was only a few years older, Richard Weickgenannt had become Franz's de facto spiritual director. He often drew on the teachings of Vincent Pallotti, founder of the Pallottine congregation to which he belonged, and from which he was on loan.

On free Thursday afternoons the two would hike together through the spruce forests and alpine meadows of the Schattseitn, in short-sleeved shirts and lederhosen, and talk endlessly of what their priestly future would hold for both of them, and especially what the future might hold for Austria.

'I can't help thinking of those lovely words from *Parsifal*,' Weickgenannt was saying, during one of those hikes. 'Remember, Franz, when the hero baptizes Kundry just before she dies?' He half-closed his eyes and murmured:

> How beautiful the meadows seem today!
> Well I recall the wondrous flowers
> Which once did try to twine themselves around me.
> Yet they did not compare with these.
> The grasses, blossoms and flowers
> Are fragrant in their innocence,
> And speak to me with loving trust

The alpine flowers were knee deep as the two men hiked across a meadow high above the Brixenbach valley – speedwell, lousewort, clematis, pasquewell, mountain avens, avalanche lily, dogwood, mountain heather. The June sun was warm on bare arms, and the men breathed deeply the meadow-fragrant air. The distant peaks gleamed.

At the fence style the two men halted and sat on the grass. Weickgenannt took a flask of coffee from one of the rucksacks. A lark sang high above.

'Just listen to that, Franz,' Weickgenannt said. 'Did you know the lark has thirteen different songs? At least, that's what the Chinese say.'

'Know something, Richard?' Franz stretched and breathed deeply. 'I haven't felt this good in a long time. I – I think I'm happy. For once. If only it could last.'

The talk turned, as it invariably did, to what might lie ahead.

'It's not just the Church, you know, that'll affect our lives,' Weickgenannt was saying. 'It's what's out there too – politics, people, the whole world changing.' He pointed north across the valley towards the Hohe Salve. 'It's what's happening beyond those mountains that sometimes bothers me. What might come out of Germany...'

'Germany?'

'There's this fellow Hitler who's just published a book,' Weickgenannt said. 'You know, that mad Austrian who was tried for treason after the Munich trouble? The book's completely daft. But I think it could be dangerous.'

'So what's he on about, exactly?'

'It's one of the most hate-filled things I've ever read – he calls it *Mein Kampf* [3] — it goes on and on about some Jewish conspiracy to take over the world. He says the Jews are "the personification of the devil and the symbol of all evil". He says they're trying to pollute what he calls the Aryan Race. By interbreeding, he says.' Weickgenannt paused to pour coffee into the cups.

'Sounds crazy to me,' Franz said.

---

[3] My Struggle

'It's crazier than you think. Can you believe it – he wants to kill off everyone who's crippled or sick or mentally ill. He says that's far more humane than keeping them alive. Can you believe that?'

'Good God. No, I can't believe it. He actually *says* that?'

'That, and lots more. You've got to destroy the weak to provide space for the strong, he says – and to keep the race pure. And that means taking over chunks of the East to get living space.'

'But sure no one's going to take that kind of talk seriously –'

'Some already do. He's already got a sizeable following – people who are sore over the Versailles Treaty and want revenge, and who regard foreigners as inferior races. He's even got followers here in Austria.'

High over the valley a bird of prey wheeled. It might have been a falcon, with those jagged wings set so far forward. The song of the lark had ceased.

'Well, God grant they never get any power.' Franz sipped thoughtfully at his coffee. 'Anyhow the churches would take a stand against such nonsense, wouldn't they? I mean, Jesus was a Jew, wasn't he?'

'I wouldn't be too sure about that. About the churches taking a stand, I mean. Did you know, they've always been in the forefront of hating the Jews? Lutherans and Catholics both. Don't we ourselves even call them "the perfidious Jews"?'

'Come on, now, Richard. That's just in the liturgy. Holy Week and all that.'

Weickgenannt turned to face Franz. ''Do you know what your own Bishop Waitz said just this month in Innsbruck? It was in the papers. He called the Jews "an alien people" who had corrupted England, France, Italy and especially America.'

'Don't mind *him*. He was always a bit of a bigot.'

'It's not just him, Franz. I can give you chapter and verse if you want. Luther called the Jews "a pest in the midst of our lands". It goes right back to the Early Fathers – John Chrysostom said the synagogue was worse than a brothel. Saint Augustine called on God to slay the Jews with his two-edged sword.'

'Ach, Richard. That was way back then. We've come a long way since those times.'

'Have we, Franz? Have we really? Did you know that not so long ago the Jesuit magazine *Civiltà Cattolica* called the Jewish nation "a giant octopus with its stomach in the banks" ? I could go on and on.'

'Well, don't! I don't want to hear any more!' Franz stood up, tossed out the rest of his coffee and glared down at Weickgenannt. 'You're not being fair to the Church, and I don't like it one bit. Those were just bigoted individuals you've quoted. I know lots of good priests who'd be nothing like that – who'd stand up and be counted. Who'd take on that Hitler fellow if it ever came to that.'

'How many do you know, Franz?'

'Lots! All those lads down there in Brixen.'

Weickgenannt was silent for a moment. He sipped his coffee and gazed down towards the town, far below in the valley. 'Can you be so sure, Franz?' he asked gently. 'Of all the priests, I mean?'

'Well, most, anyhow.'

'I wouldn't be that sure, Franz. How about those desiccated old sticks we call the dead wood in our order? Would they be any use? Or the ones who play around with women? Or with men? Or the ones who go after power to make up for their celibacy? Or spend their lives chasing money? Or the ones who've lost the Faith and daren't admit it? What use would any of *them* be?'

'But they're the exceptions, surely?'

'How do we really know, Franz, for who's going to admit it?'

A cloud had moved across the sun, and a cool breeze sprang up. The distant sounds coming up from Brixen, far below in the valley, seemed to whisper, *church, church, church.*

Franz's flash of anger had gone. 'So is that it, Richard?' he murmured. 'Is this our Church?'

'No, thank God. There's one other kind of priest. And that's the man of prayer. Of deep spirituality. Franz, it's the only way. Not just gabbling rosaries, or muttering the psalms at vespers, but daily in direct touch with God through prayer. Daily, hourly, living in the presence of God.'

Weickgenannt finished his coffee and tucked away the thermos. 'These men aren't always easy to spot,' he said, as he shouldered his rucksack. 'But the people know them instinctively.'

He stood thoughtfully gazing down the valley towards Kitzbühl, and it was as if he were talking to himself. 'They're the ones folks turn to and come away comforted, even transformed. They're the ones totally at ease with women; who love children and are loved by children; whose sermons truly inspire, not through eloquence but through sheer spirituality.'

He paused and listened for a moment, as the tinkle of cowbells came from the slopes high above. 'They're the ones in touch with God, Franz. Like the Curé of Ars. And they're the ones who'd take on those Hitlerites as a matter of conscience, if it ever came to that.'

'Are there many like that?'

'Actually I believe they're far more than we realise, because they're the quiet ones, who don't flaunt themselves. But when I'm depressed about celibacy I sometimes think of those generals in the trenches, who sent thousands over the top to die, so that a handful might take the hilltop.'

'So what can I do to reach that hilltop?'

'Like I said. Daily and unremitting prayer. Talking to God, who's all around us, and within us. But there's one other thing that I notice almost all these priests have – an extraordinary devotion to the Virgin Mary.'

8

I will place within them as a guide
My umpire Conscience, whom if they will hear,
Light after light well us'd they shall attain,
And to the end persisting, safe arrive
John Milton (Paradise Lost)

INNSBRUCK, Austria. 29 April, 1928. The first of the three steps towards the priesthood for Franz Reinisch would be the ordination to Sub Deacon, to take place in May.

When he came home to tell his family that he might not take the step, that he was thinking of leaving the seminary and giving up his studies for the priesthood, he was immensely relieved to find them accepting of such a decision.

'You can always go back to Law, Franzl,' his father said. 'You've given it a fair shot. Nothing to be ashamed of, and no one's going to blame you.' A wry chuckle. 'Ja, and there'll be some happy young lassies in the Leopoldina when they hear this.'

'I know it's only a first step, Papa, but it's a lifetime commitment. I'm just not ready for that. I just don't think I can make it.'

'Then don't, Son. Whatever God wills, we're with you. Always remember that.'

The mother was equally supportive. 'Unless you're absolutely certain, Franzl, don't go forward. And you're not certain, are you?' She took his hand. 'I'll tell you something, now. Remember that operation I had last month, Franzl? I know you prayed for me. I went though it without an anaesthetic, as a sacrifice for you, that God would guide you.'

'Oh, my God, Mutti. You *what?* Now that was crazy of you. You should never – I'm not worth that. But – but I'll never be able to thank you enough.'

BRIXEN-IM-THALE, Tyrol. 13 May, 1928. The whole Reinisch family was present in Brixen church, on the day Franz Reinisch was ordained as Sub Deacon.

Finally Franz had made his decision, and now went ahead with this first step towards the priesthood. It had been a long and lonely struggle with no one to turn to. It did not help that his friend and confidante was no longer there, Weickgenannt having been transferred to a Pallottine foundation in Boston.

Nor was it the end of the struggle, however, especially as the next two steps – these ones final and irrevocable – came in what now seems undue haste. These final steps seem to have been rushed upon Franz Reinisch, giving him very little time to think or prepare.

Ordination as Deacon came after just one month.

Then, on 29 June, the Feast of Saints Peter and Paul, Franz Reinisch was ordained to the Priesthood. The ordination was conferred by that same Bishop Sigismund Waitz who had once called the Jews 'an alien people'. That thought struck the young candidate at the very moment the anointed hands were laid upon his head.

It must have been a time of acute loneliness and anxiety. Indeed many years later Franz confided to his sister Mariedl, by then a nun, that during that time he had 'had to struggle much with evil'. He also confided that it was a newly-found trust in the Virgin Mary – learnt from Richard Weickgenannt, that had brought him through those final weeks coming up to ordination.

It was a time too for bidding a definitive farewell to the life he had known and loved. His last letter to Ludowika Linhard says as much:

Dearest Fräulein

Farewell. So ends a song. So one says when taking leave. Ja, and I must take leave from everything that has become dear and precious to me, what I carried as a gem in my heart.

I was able to spend wonderfully beautiful hours with you and they remain for me an adventure. In you I found a human heart full of sincere feeling, that showed so many lovely feelings and understanding, so that, at the very sight of you, I forgot all the common and low things of the world.

Does it lie in my power, here to say a certain 'Ja, I will take my leave' ? Is it my vocation to turn myself to the highest good that a person can strive for...?

A right hearty farewell greeting comes to you from this friend withdrawing into the distance.

Gez. ~ *Franz Reinisch*

WILTEN, Tyrol, Austria. 1 July, 1928. Legend has it that local folk, sometime in the Dark Ages, had placed a statue of the Virgin Mary under four trees in a forest. It became a place of pilgrimage, and the basilica on this site, with its statue of the Virgin under its rococo canopy of four pillars – *Unserer Lieben Frau unter den vier Säulen* [4] – is one of the most cherished places of pilgrimage in all of Austria. This is where Father Franz Reinisch celebrated his first Mass, two days after his ordination to the priesthood. (It was also where his mother and father had first caught each other's eye when they should have been saying their prayers, so perhaps it was an apt place for a new beginning.)

The event was celebrated as only the folks of the Tyrol know how: the various Wilten groups appearing in their traditional costumes, the girls in red and black overlaid with lace, petticoats galore, and a tall, veiled headdress straight out of Grimms' *Fairy Tales*; the lads in lederhosen, alpine hats with long feathers, and short green jackets with silver buttons. The students from the Leopoldina marched in their fraternity robes and caps. The Freedom Cannon of 1809 fired a salute.

---

[4] To Our Beloved Mother beneath the Four Columns

There was also a small contingent of the Innsbruck police, including young Anton Loidl. Franz was delighted to see his old childhood comrade in his proud new uniform. He didn't notice the small swastika tie-pin that Anton was wearing.

Among the letters of congratulation was one from Ireland, in which Ralph King announced that he had become a member of a missionary order, and would be ordained a priest in the following year. There was another from Richard Weickgenannt in Boston, which ended with the prophetic words, 'I would love someday to be able to greet you as one of my brethren in the Pallottines.'

A peace above all earthly dignities,
A still and quiet conscience
William Shakespeare

UNTERMERZBACH, Bavaria, Germany. 3 November, 1928. Things seemed to move fast that year, and it was a time of many changes. So it was that, barely five months after ordination, here was Franz Reinisch quitting his native Austria for Germany, to start his first evening with the Pallottine religious order, which had accepted him as a novice.

The seed planted by Weickgenannt had germinated.

'So, Reverend,' Franz said, in his easygoing Austrian way, to the novice master who had shown him to his room, 'for a start, let's smoke a cigarette together.'

Like a flash came the answer: 'Would you be so kind as to hand over all your tobacco? I'm sorry to have to tell you, but there's no smoking here in the novitiate.'

Franz had a sudden longing to hit this German bastard and wipe the smirk off his face. Instead, one hundred and fifty precious Heer & Flotte cigarettes were dragged reluctantly out of the suitcase and handed over.

What followed was a dreadful time, best understood by anyone who has tried to quit smoking. It can be even worse when one has no wish to quit, but is simply deprived of tobacco.

Franz lasted all of three weeks. It was time to get the hell out.

But how do I do it, he asks himself. This bloody novitiate with its germanic curfews and high walls is no better than a prison – and even there they'd let a fellow smoke. If I go down through the main house to the front door they'll all see me. And I can't face 'em – I'm so ashamed that I'm not man enough to stick it. Nothing else for it – I've got to run away. Like some bloody school kid.

So out into the park in that moonless November night, carrying his suitcase, looking for that tumbledown bit in the six-foot wall. The broken wall is not as low as it looked in daylight, and the first attempt to clamber over it ends in oaths and an almost sprained ankle.

Then Franz seems to hear the word *stay*. Not out loud. Not even in his head. Just – *stay*. From wherever.

Franz sits on the broken bits of wall for longer than he can remember. He gets up and hobbles along by the wall, not sure what is happening. And then, there against the far wall, is the faint outline of the white-washed Lourdes grotto.

He kneels and prays. And weeps. For a long time.

By that same month the 'mad' author of that book which has so bothered Richard Weickgenannt, had managed to get 108,000 due-paying members into his political party – the National Socialist German Workers' Party [5] – now popularly known as *Naziism* [6] or the *Nazis*. And the party was growing fast. But it was more than a party: it was almost an alternative religion that offered hope, visions and dreams. *And also hate.*

Although relatively few had read the book – it was quite unreadable – the ideas in Adolf Hitler's *Mein Kampf* were spreading rapidly throughout Germany via the *Völkischer Beobachter* [7] newspaper, through the brilliant propaganda of one Josef Goebbels, through the *Hitler Jugend* [8], and the parades of the brown-shirted *Sturm Abteilung* [9] organization.

As George Orwell said about *Mein Kampf*: 'Human beings don't only want comfort, safety, short working hours, hygiene, birth control and, in general, common sense: they also, at least intermittently, want struggle and self-sacrifice, not to mention drums, flags, and loyalty parades.'

The man who founded the Pallottine Congregation of priests died long before his work was finished. Not that it ever could be finished. When Vincent Pallotti was buried in 1850, people said his apostolate was destined to failure. But his answer on his deathbed was this: 'I have done all *I* can. Others will finish it. The hand of the Lord is not shortened.'

---

[5] *Nationalsozialistische Deutsche Arbeiterpartei (NSDAP)*
[6] Short for *Nationalsozialismus*
[7] People's Observer
[8] Hitler Youth
[9] Storm Division or Storm Troopers

Whatever had happened at that grotto brought a subtle change in Franz Reinisch, and he began to feel that he might have at least a part in finishing Pallotti's task. Or continuing it, for such a task is never finished.

Exactly what task? Back in the 1840s Vincent Pallotti had been accused of renewing the Reformation attack on the Catholic priesthood, simply because he insisted that ordinary layfolk also can bring Christ to the world. Some of the clergy of the time didn't like that, as they felt their ascendancy threatened.

So the task Franz took on was precisely that: to get everyone – not just priests – involved in bringing people to God.

'Without Love there is no apostolate,' Pallotti had said. And his other favourite saying was: 'Do not be stingy – be generous with your God.'

Whereas a favourite saying of Adolf Hitler was 'Hate is more lasting than dislike.' And also, 'I do not see why man should not be just as cruel as nature.'

It was the word 'generous' that seemed to resonate for Franz. Duty was one thing: generosity was something far more. Whether it was in the simple community things like giving up time to conducting the choir, or helping to involve layfolk in local parish work, or counselling a younger confrère, it became his aim to be generous.

And there was certainly need for generosity in controlling that choleric temper. The teutonic rigidity of the community was hard to take. There were flare-ups and apologies, and earnest prayers at the grotto for the gift of self-control.

Something must have worked, for by the end of the novitiate Franz was known for his kindness and cheerful temperament.

Well, mostly.

Yet during those two years there were times of despondency even verging on breakdown. Recurring illnesses, of the ear and of the gut, adding to the depression, brought despair of ever reaching the heights of holiness that the novice master insisted on putting before them as an ideal.

Finally the words of a retreat master, that everyone must find his own way to God, and in his own time, brought a measure of peace. 'Just doing the ordinary things extraordinarily well,' as Sainte Thérèse had said. Franz settled for the long haul, letting holiness take its time.

Which it did.

10

Neither a nation nor an individual
can surrender conscience
to another's keeping
Theodore Roosevelt

BERLIN, Germany, 29 October, 1929. If Gustav Stresemann had not died just before the Wall Street Crash, perhaps Germany might have fared better, as he was the man who had restored the country's economy and stabilized the Republic.

But that was not to be. Instead the land lurched from one crisis to another, with industry grinding to a halt, world markets for German goods drying up, loans coming due, workers laid off, inflation, banks collapsing, middle-class families reduced to beggary – the Great Depression.

A disaster for Germany, but a boon for Adolf Hitler. For a people reduced to misery will listen to anyone who can promise hope.

UNTERMERZBACH, Bavaria. December 1930. When the two novitiate years were up, the Pallottines paid Franz the compliment of appointing him to lecture their students in philosophy. This revealed for the first time a quite remarkable gift for communication which, in the years to come, was to take him far. Very far indeed.

One might even say, to his death. But that was later.

The student was now the teacher. Franz Reinisch rapidly gained a name as a sharp thinker with a clear gift of discernment. He regarded teaching not just as the packing of minds with facts or theories, but as the development of creativity and of spirituality in his students.

To encourage clear thinking he introduced the weekly *disputatio*, with defender and attacker, in which a student had to present a thesis and then have to face attempts to demolish it by his opponent. It could get heated at times.

As educator rather than teacher Franz could be effective. Years later one of his students recalled a sample of such education: 'Once he gave me a *bene* [OK] for a test. In all the other tests I had got an *eminenter* [outstanding]. I got mad, and he seemed to be delighted with that. Later he told me he had deliberately hoodwinked me to give me a little experience of misery so as to deepen my ascetic life.'

After two years of this work, the teacher became once more a student, when he was transferred to Salzburg to take his final year in theology. After that his formal studies came to an end. Learning, however, continued, but now it was about the wider world beyond the cloister. He was to learn a great deal, and very fast, and much of it distressed him.

BERLIN, Friedrichshain, Germany. 14 January, 1930. 10.04 p.m. Twenty-two-year-old Nazi storm trooper Horst Wessel is shot in the face by communists outside the flat where he lives with his prostitute girlfriend. On 23 February he dies in hospital from blood poisoning contracted there. His coffin is paraded across Berlin for many hours; the red-white-and-black *Hakenkreuz* [10] flag flies everywhere in spite of the banning by police; and a poem written by Horst Wessel (*Die Fahne hoch*[11]) is sung, to a melody adapted from a Salvation Army hymn:

> The flag on high! The ranks are tightly closed!
> The SA marches with quiet, steady step.
> Comrades shot by the Red Front and reactionaries
> March in spirit within our ranks [12]

Nazi leaders told their people that Horst Wessel would watch over them from beyond the grave, and would be a hell of a sight more efficacious than any Virgin Mary. In the years that followed, the song by this martyr Nazi became the anthem of the Nazi party, and later practically the second national anthem of Germany.

BERLIN, Germany. 13 March, 1932. *Freedom and Bread* was the slogan the Nazis employed in their aim to get Hitler elected

---

[10] Literally, *Hooked Cross*. Called *Swastika* in English, a word from Sanskrit. It is a symbol that goes back to Neolithic times, and is a Symbol of auspiciousness in Hinduism, Buddhism and Jainism. Adolf Hitler personally selected it and refined the design as the symbol of the Nazis. It later became the flag of the Third Reich.

[11] 'The Flag on high'

[12] *Die Fahne hoch! Die Reihen fest geschlossen!*
SA marschiert mit ruhig festem Schritt.
Kam'raden, die Rotfront und Reaktion erschossen,
Marschier'n im Geist in unser'n Reihen mit

president of Germany, in place of tired old Hindenburg. The slogan was apt, with six million people unemployed, whole families starving, communism poised to strike, chaos in Munich and Berlin. And people listened, with eleven million choosing Adolf Hitler as their Saviour.

It wasn't quite enough, of course, with Hindenburg's prestige winning him eighteen million votes. In the runoff that followed, Hitler won over another two million, giving him 36 per cent of the vote. That still wasn't enough, but it showed that the 'mad' author of *Mein Kampf* had arrived.

'Weickgenannt was right,' was Franz Reinisch's comment when the election results were carried on Austrian radio. 'That fellow's not going away. All I can say is, thank God this is Austria, not Germany.'

He would soon however be back in Germany.

11

Were a true representation of our lives to be flashed before your mind's eye,
you would think yourself watching a city taken by storm, in which all regard
for modesty and right had been abandoned, and the only
counsel was that of force
Seneca

FRIEDBERG, near Augsburg, Germany. 21 July, 1933. At the provincial house of the Pallottines, the young postulants who sought acceptance into the congregation had first to prove their worth by helping out in everyday tasks around house and offices.

Young Ernst Wendl from Munich was alone in the kitchen, scrubbing pots when everyone else was off working elsewhere. He heard someone playing the harmonium in the nearby dining room. As he said later: 'It was a melody so tender and melancholy that it could get right under your skin. It was like an inner prayer.'

He went in to find out who was playing. It was Franz Reinisch, who immediately stopped when he realised someone was listening.

'That's so sad, Father,' young Wendl said. 'But it's beautiful. Would you play it again? Please?'

Franz shrugged. 'I'm not sure exactly what it was I was playing,' he said, turning away.

'What's wrong, Father? Are you OK? You don't seem yourself.'

'I'm fine, thanks, Brother. Just a bit fatigued.' But his eyes had filled up with tears.

'Father, could I suggest –'

'Brother Ernst. Please – just – leave me *alone!* OK?'

When that tone entered Franz Reinisch's voice, you left him alone. Pronto.

One couldn't really let oneself down in front of youngsters, but the fact was that Franz Reinisch was suffering once again from depression. And it was getting worse by the day.

There was good reason for his depression.

Only the day before, he had learnt of what seemed to be a sell-out by his church to Hitler. Word had come through of a *Concordat* – a formal agreement or treaty between the Vatican and the new Nazi regime. Some of Franz's confrères were delighted with what they saw as peace and freedom for their church – freedom for the Catholic press, free communications between Rome and the bishops, freedom for professional and youth organizations. A church safe and supported by the new regime.

'But can't you see it's a sell-out?' Franz had argued hotly to his brethren during an after-lunch recreation hour. 'Those promises will never be kept. Listen to that bastard Hitler himself – didn't he write about the Big Lie [*die grosse Lüge*]? Didn't he say you could make a lie so colossal that no one would believe that someone would dare make it up? Mark my words – within a year he'll break every single promise.'

No one believed that of course.

It had been one of the most deeply depressing years in the life of Franz Reinisch. He had to watch helplessly as the Nazi tentacles slithered around everything precious and free in Germany and then tightened in to strangle.

It began when the Austrian Bishop Gföllner of Linz issued a pastoral which was read out in all the churches of the diocese. The key phrase was, 'You cannot be a true Nazi and a good Catholic.' This was reassuring, until the pastoral went on to make a ferocious attack on the Jews, saying it is the duty of Christians to combat Jewish influence. In the Middle Ages this was accomplished by confining the Jews to ghettos, the bishop said. But this is unnecessary today, as legislation can eliminate their influence and prevent them from flooding the world with demoralization.

If church hierarchy was talking like this, to whom could Franz really turn? Never had he felt so alone.

On 30 January, 1933, Hitler had got himself appointed Chancellor of Germany. On 28 February, after the Reichstag fire, he abolished civil liberties with his so-called Fire Decree. On 24 March he brought in the Enabling Act[13] which gave him power to enact laws without consulting parliament. That same month the Nazis established a camp at Dachau to lock up their

---

[13] *Gesetz zur Behebung der Not von Volk und Reich* (Law to Remedy the Distress of People and Reich)

opponents in what they called 'protective custody'. They made no secret of it, as it was an excellent means of intimidation.

On 1 April of that year Hitler instigated a boycott of Jewish businesses. On 10 May came the burning of books in the presence of hundreds of thousands of students, at 32 university towns throughout the Reich – including books by James Joyce, Victor Hugo, Jack London, John dos Passos, Hemingway, Brecht, Eric Remarque, Stephan Zweig, Joseph Conrad, André Gide, Upton Sinclair, HG Wells, Aldous Huxley, Dostoyevsky, Tolstoy, Albert Einstein, Freud, Kafka, and Helen Keller – with Goebbels declaiming, 'You do well in this midnight hour to commit to the flames the evil spirit of the past. This is a strong, great and symbolic deed... These flames not only illuminate the final act of the old era, they also light up the new. Never before have our young men had so good a right to clean up the debris of the past... Oh my century, it is a joy to be alive.'

In his lectures around that time, Franz Reinisch was regularly heard to quote from *An Open Letter to German Students*, written by Helen Keller, herself blind, deaf and dumb:

> You may burn my books, and the books of the best minds in
> Europe, but the ideas those books contain have passed
> through millions of channels and will go on.

Then, in July, almost at the same time as the Concordat with the Vatican, all political parties except the Nazis were banned. To an Austrian exile like Franz Reinisch, the terrifying things that were happening, and in such rapid succession, made him feel that Germany had become a giant prison cell, and that he was incarcerated in it.

To match this outer awfulness, there was also the inner torment of a man feeling isolated, lonely and useless. Even his priesthood seemed to recede into meaninglessness. Is this all there is to it? Teaching young idiots who haven't a clue about anything? Not a soul in the world to love? How could I love these dreary confrères going about their duties without a spark of creativity?

What have I in common with them? Creativity? *Quatsch.* Well, have I any? Am I one whit better? Where's *my* creativity? Sure, I'm marvellous with the image – me the great, humorous, competent, likeable, musical, assured humbug. The secret grouch.

Keep it hidden, of course. Same old pride and arrogance I can never shake off. Prayer life dried up. God, if they only knew me. Papa was right – I'm completely unsuitable for the priesthood. Maybe it's time to go over the wall again.

But there isn't even a wall here. Yes, there is – the wall's in my head now. I'm my own jailer. I'm trapped. God, how did they do this to us? My own jailer – no need for bars. Or walls.

A timid knock on the door. Young Wendl there.

'Sorry to disturb you, Father,' the youngster whispered. 'But I thought this might interest you.' He handed him a flimsy magazine. 'It's from our Vallendar house – that Schönstatt society.'

Sal Terrae was the title of the magazine – Latin for 'Salt of the Earth'. Franz sat down on his bed, opened the amateurish-looking pages and glanced at the contents.

Two and a half hours later, when the bell rang for Matins, he was still reading. And after prayers he went straight back up to read more.

Much of the stuff was written by a fellow Pallottine called Josef Kentenich, who claimed that the Catholic Church had grown petrified and rigid with its bureaucratic structures and lack of freedom. 'We must be free characters,' Kentenich insisted. 'God wants no galley-slaves: he wants free oarsmen.' He called for a church and indeed a world culture based on the fundamental structure of love.

Kentenich kept going on about Divine Providence – that God actually keeps us in existence every instant, and that He's directly present in every single thing that happens at every moment in our lives. It's something we've mostly forgotten or vaguely assent to, Kentenich said. But if we can actually realise it, be aware of it, our lives are transformed. Because then every single thing has a meaning.

And the other thing Kentenich kept stressing was that every family has a mother, and a mother's job is to care for each of her children, day in, day out. 'But we believers are one great family, and this family too has a mother. We call her Mary. She happens also to be God's mother as well.'

In later years Franz described reading this pamphlet as 'a Eureka moment'.

ROME, Vatican City. 26 July, 1933. The ink was hardly dry on the Concordat when the Vatican paper *L'Osservatore Romano* found it necessary to protest against violations of the agreement. And in October Pope Pius XI spoke out clearly about his fears, to a German pilgrimage of the Catholic Young Men's Society:

> We must lay up great hopes in our hearts. But, beloved sons, our hopes cannot exclude every danger. You know that we are filled with the deepest anxiety and real alarm about the youth of Germany, and entertain fears with regard to religion in Germany.[14]

Franz Reinisch's fears were already being echoed at the very centre of his church. It was already clear that all denominational youth organizations were to be dissolved, and all their members forced into the nationwide Hitler Youth. And in December of that year came the *Schriftleitergesetz* [15] which forced editors of religious magazines and daily papers into a Literary Chamber of the Reich, and excluded from publication 'anything likely to weaken the will for union of the German people and German culture.' Indeed, after the promulgation of the law, the very existence of a catholic daily press was deemed disloyalty to the new state: 'There are no longer Catholic or Evangelical editors, but only German editors... National Socialism does not suffer this fundamental principle to be

---

[14] Johann Neuhäusler. *Persecution of Catholic Church in Third Reich. p.2*
[15] Law Concerning Editors

shaken or distorted,' as an editorial in the *Nationalzeitung* declared.[16]

[16] *Nationalzeitung*, No. 92, 1934.

12

We become equally responsible for the actions of others
the instant we become conscious
of what they are doing wrong
but remain silent
Suzy Kassem

BERLIN, Saturday, 30 June, 1934. Two young Americans had gone on a date to a private lake in Gross Glienike just outside the city. One was Martha Dodd, daughter of the US ambassador. It was a beautifully warm day and, as they drove back to town, 'our heads giddy and our bodies burning from the sun,' they had the top down on their Ford roadster.

Something seemed different as they drove into the city around 6 p.m. The place was eerily silent. There was hardly anyone on the streets, except for the black uniforms of the SS and the field grey of the military. There wasn't a sign of the brown shirts of the Storm Troopers, which were usually everywhere. Trucks and barriers filled the streets, but the car's diplomatic plates allowed the young couple through. When they got to her darkened home a frightened young Martha rushed upstairs, into the arms of her brother.

'Where have you been, Martha?' he cried. 'We've all been so worried. Von Schleicher's been shot. And so has Strasser. They say they're murdering everyone. There's martial law in Berlin.'

FRIEDBERG, near Augsburg, Germany. 1 July, 1934. Hitler's voice was shrill as it rose and fell over the crackling radio: 'In this hour I was responsible for the fate of the German people, and thereby I became the supreme judge of the German people. I gave the order to shoot the ringleaders in this treason,' he ranted. 'Let the nation know that its existence – which depends on its internal order and security – cannot be threatened with impunity by anyone! And let it be known for all time to come that if anyone raises his hand to strike the State, then certain death is his lot –'

Franz leaned over and switched off the radio.

There was a squawk from the other priests in the common room. 'Hey, Franz. What'd you do that for? Put it back on!'

'They're a bunch of thugs!' Franz hissed. 'They've murdered hundreds without even a trial. Just to get rid of Röhm. It's just a crowd of gangsters falling out – for that's what they are – gangsters that have Germany by the balls. If you want to listen to that bastard, go ahead and listen.' He stood up and stalked out of the room.

'You'll get yourself in trouble yet, Franz,' one of the priests yelled after him.

'Let him, if he wants to,' another said. 'Trouble is, he could get us into trouble too. He doesn't seem to have heard of those Gestapo fellows. They've got ears everywhere now.'

'Well, hopefully not in this room, thank God.'

'You sure?'

BERLIN, 9 a.m. 2 August, 1934. After a long struggle with cancer, death came to 87-year-old German President Hindenburg. Within hours the Nazi-controlled legislature had enacted the following:

> Section 1. The office of Reich President will be combined with that of Reich Chancellor. The existing authority of the Reich President will consequently be transferred to the Führer and Reich Chancellor, Adolf Hitler. He will select his deputy.
>
> Section 2. This law is effective as of the time of the death of Reich President von Hindenburg.

Although it was totally and utterly illegal, Adolf Hitler by the middle of 1934 was now supreme ruler of Germany. He took the title of *Führer*, which simply means 'Leader'.

On 19 August Germany went to the polls to ratify this seizure of power, and gave Hitler 90 per cent of the vote.

Depart, Commander. Enter now into Valhalla. Hitler's words, addressed to the sarcophagus at the state funeral of President Hindenburg, were noble as befits a great occasion and a great orator.

85

But there was nothing noble about the confidence trick now pulled on the whole German Army. As part of the ceremony the soldiers present were asked to renew their military oath – the *Fahneneid*. The oath should normally read:

> I swear by God this sacred oath, that I will faithfully and honestly serve my People and Fatherland and, as a brave soldier, be ready to offer my life for this oath.

However there was an ever-so-slight change this time. The oath which was given these soldiers to read went as follows:

> I swear by God this sacred oath: I will render unconditional obedience to Adolf Hitler, the Führer of the German Reich and people, Supreme Commander of the Armed Forces, and, as a brave soldier, be ready to offer my life at any time for this oath.

And that was how it remained during the eleven years until the Third Reich came to its bloody end.

It took considerable time before the knowledge of this crucial alteration percolated to the general public, as it had not exactly been trumpeted in the newspapers.

Franz Reinisch was close to apoplexy when he learned of it. 'Swear an oath to that criminal? Never!' He was talking to Father Kerstein who had learnt it from a cousin in the military. 'Do you realise what it would mean to take this oath? You'd be

School class photo at the Leopoldinium, Hall, Tyrol (Franciscan Fathers), c.1915.
Franz Reinisch is centre front row (fifth from left).

Photo courtesy Franz Reinisch Forum, Schönstatt

calling on God to witness that you're giving total obedience to a criminal who has murdered and cheated and lied. You couldn't, simply couldn't take an oath to that scoundrel. Your conscience couldn't allow it.' He sighed. 'Though I'm not sure you should ever promise total obedience to anyone. You'd be putting your conscience in your arse pocket.'

'So what about the obedience priests promise to their bishop?' Father Kerstein asked.

'Ja, indeed. That could be tricky too. There's a limit to all obedience, and the limit is your conscience.'

13

There are some who... close their eyes and ears to the injustice around them.
Only at the cost of self-deception can they keep their private blamelessness
clean from the stains of responsible action in the world
Dietrich Bonhoeffer

SCHÖNSTATT, Rhineland-Palatinate, Germany. 17 August, 1934. Six miles downriver from where the Moselle enters the Rhine, the Westerwald opens into a deep-cut valley which a document of 1143 describes as *eyne schoene stat* – 'a beautiful place'. The district and town has the name of Vallendar, but the monastery here has kept the name of 'the beautiful place' — Schönstatt. At 7 p.m. in this August evening a line of cars, plus a truck containing two bodies, arrived at Schönstatt.

The bodies were those of Hans Wormer and Max Brunner, German soldiers killed in battle in France in 1917. They had been sodality members of the Schönstatt movement before enlisting, and were regarded as young men of considerable dedication or even piety – 'hero sodalists' was the term used. The thinking behind the re-interment seems to have been to set a counter example to the growing Nazi influence on Germany's youth.

Outside the tiny Schönstatt shrine – the Chapel of Grace, as he called it – Father Josef Kentenich spoke the words of welcome to the two deceased. 'You have conquered a place in the heart of the whole Schönstatt movement,' he said. 'Hear a warm *Deo Gratias* from the lips of all who have found a home here, as well as from my own lips.' Then he turned to the hundreds gathered for the occasion: 'Remain true to the spirit of the Hero Sodalists... Remain true to the heroic spirit that created our whole work in the beginning, and which we now serve!'

This was Franz's first sight of Father Josef Kentenich, who had founded the Schönstatt movement in 1914. The massive white beard to the chest gave the impression of an Old-Testament prophet, and the eyes behind those rimless spectacles seemed to look right through you. Indeed those eyes could do just that, and could even change a man.

Which is what they did to Franz Reinisch during the four weeks he spent in Schönstatt at that time. 'When you're gone from here, you'll find that God's Mother has stolen your heart,' Kentenich told him when he was leaving.

Whether God's Mother did it, or Josef Kentenich did it, Franz was a changed man. Changed once again, for he had already gone through so many changes in his life. Gone was the depression, to return only occasionally. 'All my thoughts and wishes are focused on Schönstatt,' he wrote in a letter to Kentenich, after his return to Salzburg. As spiritual director of the theology students here, he said, he was 'carefully instilling the riches of Schönstatt thinking in the formation of the young Pallottines'.

What exactly was he instilling?

The Schönstatt movement was not considered altogether kosher in the Roman Catholic Church of those years. Kentenich's provocative personality had not made friends in high places. Nor, from the very beginning, did his outspoken assertions. 'He is walking dangerous ways,' had been the comment of his superiors, as far back as his 1908 studies in Limburg.

It was regarded as arrogance that Kentenich should regard the tiny Shrine at Schönstatt as a kind of national focal point: 'In the shadow of the Shrine, the destiny of the Church in Germany and beyond will be essentially decided for the next centuries.'

Words like that did not make friends.

And all this talk about tabernacles – 'It is good for us to be here. Here we want to build tabernacles. Here is our favourite place' – sounded a bit too like Christ's Transfiguration on the mountaintop to fall easily on the ears of eminent churchmen.

However the main objection to Schönstatt in Germany was its unequivocal stress on devotion to the Virgin Mary. Many thought it was completely exaggerated, and that Christ was being moved aside from the centre of the Faith. As Jesuit liturgist Josef A. Jungmann said: 'We don't need a Marian movement, but one focused on Christ.'

Kentenich's answer to this was: 'We need a Marian movement that consciously seeks and strives after Christ.'

There were a lot of other things that annoyed the churchmen. They did not like the fact that the Schönstatt communities did not take vows, but just made 'a covenant of love with Our Lady of Schönstatt'. Worse still, one could quit after three months' notice, without asking Rome. And the movement's stress on freedom and initiative bothered authorities who feared that obedience would suffer.

Whatever about the views among the German bishops and the Roman cardinals, Franz Reinisch took to the Schönstatt spirituality as if he were born to it. Especially the emphasis on devotion to the Virgin Mary. And this was 'the riches of the Schönstatt thinking' that he was instilling in the theology students at Salzburg.

NUREMBERG, Germany. 5 September, 1934. Every religious movement seems to have a sacred centre – Mecca is the focal point for Muslims; Rome for Catholics; Jerusalem for the Jews. As was Nuremberg for the Nazis. It was the 1934 Nazi Party Rally in that gothic city that made clear to the world that this was as much a religious as a political movement, and that the rally was a pilgrimage.

One million people were in Nuremberg for those few days, and the religious, prophetic atmosphere was palpable, with its torchlight processions, hymns, banners and pageantry. 'The German form of life is definitely determined for the next thousand years,' were Hitler's words. The chant of the massed crowds was essentially religious: '*Sieg Heil, Sieg Heil, Sieg*

Heil.[17] We want one Leader! Nothing for us – all for Germany. Heil Hitler!'

Of this new religion, Hitler was the Messiah. American journalist William L. Shirer was there on the first day of the rally. 'I was a little shocked at the faces,' he wrote later, 'when Hitler finally appeared on the balcony for a moment. They reminded me of the crazed expressions I once saw in the back country of Louisiana on the faces of some Holy Rollers... they looked up at him as if he were a Messiah, their faces transformed into something positively inhuman.'

Hitler's messiah image was not just an aberration of simple folk, but was carefully nurtured by the Nazi regime. 'Germany has been transformed into a great house of the Lord, where the Führer as our Mediator stand before the throne of God,' declared Goebbels. 'We believe on this earth in Adolf Hitler alone! We believe in National Socialism as the creed which is the sole source of Grace' – words of Robert Ley. According to Baldur von Schirach, 'He who serves Adolf Hitler, our Führer, serves Germany, and he who serves Germany, serves God.'

Hitler himself half believed it: 'I nearly imagined myself to be Jesus Christ when he came to his Father's temple and found it full of money-changers,' he said, referring to his first arrival in Berlin.

What distressed Franz more than anything was an article in the *Westdeutscher Beobachter*:

> Yesterday witnessed the profession of the Religion of the Blood in all its imposing reality.

---

[17] Hail victory

Yesterday saw the triumphant and decisive beginning of our fight to make National Socialism the only racial religion of the German people. Whoever has sworn his oath of allegiance to Hitler has pledged himself until death to this sublime idea. There is no more room for doubts and uncertainties, no room for retreat.

If this was the new religion, what was to become of the old? And what did this new religion actually believe in? These were the questions that agonized Franz Reinisch, that filled his thoughts and guided his utterances in the coming months and years. Those utterances turned out to be dangerous.

It soon became apparent that this new religion was also a religion of fear – a fear comparable to that of the Inquisition, but far more pervasive. People began to fear to speak their thoughts; parents grew fearful of their children, who might be led to betray them; mutual trust withered; joy evaporated; fear could be tasted and smelt. The Gestapo[18] were the modern-day inquisitors. And while the Gestapo lurked, Dachau loomed.

---

[18] Secret State Police – *Geheime Staatspolitzei*, abbreviated to the acronym *Ge-sta-po*

14

SALZBURG, Austria. October 1934. After Franz Reinisch's return to the house of studies here, his new enthusiasm for Schönstatt did not please all of his fellow Pallottines. Nor did his outspokenness about the Nazi regime. His all-or-nothing attitude in everything, and his lack of diplomacy, did not always make disciples and made many people uneasy. It certainly did not help when he was heard to say, 'Whoever wants to be a true Pallottiner, must be a Schönstätter.'

It particularly irked some of the older members of the community who found this relatively young upstart and his views hard to take. Indeed some of them began to regard the Schönstätters as a sort of lunatic fringe of the Pallottines.

'There's a bit too much of this Virgin Mary thing,' Father Vogels was heard to say. 'I mean, we all have devotion to Mary, but this Mother-Thrice-Admirable stuff is a bit over the top. I mean, are they forgetting about Christ? They're a bunch of fanatics, if you ask me.'

There were quite a few arguments, some of which brought out that temper which Franz Reinisch spent his life trying to control. And then would immediately come the apology which was usually graciously accepted. The man's sincerity and innate kindness was so patent that one couldn't but like him.

Much of the tension came from Franz's championing of Protestant theologian Karl Barth. As rector of Bonn University Barth had been required to take an oath to Hitler personally, an oath similar to the one required of the military:

> I swear, to the Führer of the German Reich and People, Adolf Hitler, to be loyal and obedient, and to scrupulously carry out my official duties, so help me God

Barth refused, unless he were allowed to add the words – ...*in so far as I can answer for the Gospel of Christ*. This of course was not acceptable to the regime. Barth was fired from his post and had to return to his native Switzerland. Had he been German he might have fared worse.

There were ructions in the Pallottine community, especially among the German members, with Dieter Vogels insisting on the need for a mental reservation in all such oaths – where the swearer silently added a proviso similar to the one refused to Barth. 'Dammit, man, we may all have to face an oath like that sooner or later. They're already concocting one for the bishops.

We'll need to add words like Barth's, but only in our hearts. Silently.'

'And that would be a *lie!*' Franz was cold and hard and grim-faced.

'It's easy for you –'

'Let me quote you Barth, brother.' Franz pulled a magazine from his soutane pocket and read:

> Hitler demands this oath as a duty, that the swearer, with flesh and hair, with body and soul, should sell himself to this man – over whom there is no constitution, no right and law – whom from the outset he must absolutely trust that under all circumstances he knows, wants, and can achieve what is best for Germany and for me personally, and that I accept from him that he could lead me into a conflict, in which he has wrong and I have right. To do this would already be a betrayal.

Franz slammed the magazine down on the table. 'What d'you think of that, brother?'

'It's not that simple –'

'It *is* that simple. Let me tell you something, Brother. I will never take an oath to that bastard. What's more, I will never blaspheme God by swearing an oath that includes a lie!'

'You may have to decide sooner than you think.'

'I've already decided.'

The reality of this new religion of fear came home to Franz Reinisch when his provincial superior, Father Josef Frank, summoned him from Austria to the head house in Germany, at Friedberg.

The Gestapo, it seemed, had come calling.

The provincial's office was chilly and smelt of wax floor polish. For some reason in later years that smell always seemed to conjure up, for Franz, a sense of the Gestapo about to come calling once more.

'I want you, Father, please, to be more circumspect in what you say,' Frank was saying. 'We've had complaints about your lectures and your sermons.'

'What sort of complaints, Father?'

A sigh. 'To be honest, it's hard to be sure what's bothering them. I think it's just – that you're so forthright and open.'

'You want me not to be forthright? Not to be open? You mean, to be closed? And what would closed mean?'

'I don't know what to say, Father. Just please be careful. Remember what you say involves us too. No one is safe anymore.'

'But surely, Father, we must heed what the Pope said at Easter? That we should always speak the truth and defend the rights of conscience? Besides, I'm in Austria – surely I can speak freely there.'

Frank shook his head sadly. 'Not even there, Father. Their eyes and ears are everywhere.'

It distressed Franz to see that even his religious superior was a frightened man.

The realization that no one is safe came forcibly home to Franz almost immediately. On the train back to Austria, all had to dismount at the Freilassing border checkpoint. As the passengers waited on the freezing windswept station platform, two men in plain clothes came up to Franz and beckoned him out of the line. One wore that creaking leather overcoat which later became the badge of the secret police, rendering them hardly secret but certainly intimidating. Franz was taken to an office in the station building and put through a lengthy interrogation.

'Where have you been in Germany?

'Your business there?

'Whom did you meet?

'Did you give lectures while in Germany?

'Where, and to whom?

'What is your destination now?'

He was detained long after the train had left, and told he could thank his Austrian citizenship that he wasn't perhaps arrested. It was a thoroughly shaken Franz Reinisch who caught a 3 a.m. train to Salzburg.

On his return home he found a letter from his old school friend Kurt Schuschnigg, now Chancellor of Austria since the murder of Dollfuss in July. 'I fear for my life every day,' the letter read. 'My dear friend, be careful. Watch your words. And your friends too. No one is safe now, not even here in Austria...'

Franz found himself wondering if the Gestapo had read even this.

15

In my opinion, it is you considerate, humane men, that are responsible
for all the brutality and outrage wrought by these wretches;
because, if it were not for your sanction and influence,
the whole system could not keep
foothold for an hour
Harriet Beecher Stowe

VIENNA, Austria. 17 June, 1935. Austrian Chancellor Schuschnigg was in the deepest depression as he sat with Franz Reinisch in his study at the Ballhausplatz, after returning from the funeral of his wife. Both men were nursing shots of *doppeltgebrannter*, Franz with his customary cigarette. The clang of a tram came up from the street below.

'What's it all about, Franz? Don't give me any of your pious claptrap about the Virgin Mary and God's will and all that. Did God make Herma's car crash? Did he inspire those bastards to murder Dollfuss and land me in this bloody job? Is he whispering in Hitler's ear right now?'

'What do you believe, Kurt? I mean, really?'

'How do you mean?'

'Are you still a Catholic?'

'What do you mean? Of course I am.'

'You mean, you were born one. Not the same thing. If you'd been born Jewish, you'd be reading the Torah right now. Remember there's a measure of truth in every faith.'

'Well, I wasn't born Jewish. So I'm Catholic, and that's it.'

Franz paused to light another Heer & Flotte. 'Do you still believe in Krampus and Santa Claus, Kurt? No, of course you don't. So why go on believing in the Virgin Mary? Or Jesus Christ, for that matter? Just because you learned it from your parents doesn't make it true.'

'I thought you were a priest, Franz.'

'Would you listen to me. Sooner or later in a man's life, if he has any sense at all, he must ask if it's all just a yarn. I did. It's part of growing up. I mean, the whole thing's very hard to take – God becomes Man; so God must have a mother; Jesus rising from the dead. I mean, come on! But, as they say, there's enough light to see and enough darkness to doubt. When you reach that point, it's a leap in the dark: *Lord I believe: help thou my unbelief.* As Thomas said to Jesus.'

There was silence between the two men.

'But you don't make that leap alone, Kurt. You get a special grace from God to make it. And you have to ask for that grace, even if you're not sure there's anyone to ask. Do you know what my first prayer is, every morning? *Lord, that I may see.*'

'Isn't that a bit of a contradiction? Asking from someone that mightn't be there? Like shouting into the dark?'

'It *is* a contradiction. And it's only when the gift of Faith comes that it's resolved. Or rather, it's never resolved. But with

Faith you somehow *know*. In the strangest way, you know. For some people it's a profound experience that suddenly comes. For others, it just slowly grows. It's there in the Scriptures – *Faith is the substance of things hoped for, the evidence of things not seen* – Hebrews 11, if I remember rightly.'

'Virgin Mary, and all that stuff?'

'Oh, does it really matter whether she's a virgin? She's the mother of God, and my mother too. Our mother. She looks after us. That's all that matters.'

'But Franz, isn't Jesus enough? Why do we need to bring his mother into it?'

Franz stubbed out his cigarette and leaned back. 'Because she's feminine, Kurt.'

'What's that supposed to mean?'

'Kurt, look at this Nazi doctrine that's creating such hell everywhere. What is it but the Rule of the Male? It's totally masculine – dominance, control, hate, war – you name it. All those male things that have wrecked the world since time began.

'So, what are the marks of the Feminine? Compassion, above all. Love; nurturing; care; sympathy; empathy; pity. Gentleness. We need those things more than ever before. We've always needed them: long before Christianity men were looking to the Feminine – Astarte, Venus, Aphrodite. The Nordics had Freya. Even the Celts had Cliodhna. Why do you think that was?'

'That we need the Feminine?'

'Exactly. And don't forget, God's the best of all psychologists. He knew what we needed, and that's why he gave us Mary.'

'Do you honestly really pray to her?'

'I do, Kurt. Day in, day out. And, Kurt, I'm certain I'm heard.'

'So where do I go from here?'

'You start with, *Lord that I may see.* It's the one prayer that's absolutely guaranteed an answer.'

CONSTANCE, Germany. 14 July, 1935. When Frau Strasser heard that there was a new priest over at St. Joseph's Student House, a Father Reinisch, she thought perhaps he might be willing to take over direction of the small girls' group she was looking after. The group was affiliated to Schönstatt.

'As we stood across from him in the library,' she later recalled, 'my courage sank. This tall, lean man, with the piercing eyes and his short way of speaking, surely would want to know nothing of us. I said to him that we had heard he was a Schönstatt priest and we wanted to ask him something. When he heard we were affiliated to Schönstatt his immediate words were, "For Schönstatt I will do anything".'

Unfortunately he was able to do very little because shortly afterwards he became ill with kidney trouble and, later, shingles.

As Franz himself put it, sickness was his silent suffering that often hindered the message he felt bound to deliver. In his new assignments – to promote the missions and to work with young men's groups – he found himself returning regularly to that message. He saw it as his role to warn against the ever-accelerating influence of Naziism.

In 1935 that influence was growing more baleful by the day. As Pope Pius XI said on 22 April, 'Efforts are being made to de-Christianize Germany and lead her back to barbarous paganism.' [19]

In theory the Nazis encouraged *Gottgläubigkeit* [20] – belief in a vague sort of 'higher power', a belief that was little more than paganism. This paganism was a return to an imagined pre-christian Germany, where the race had been pure and undiluted; where the Volk and the Land were mystically united, with the land the blood-source of the people – 'Blood and Soil' (*Blut und Boden*, shortened to *Blubo*); where posterity was the only immortality; where Might was Right; where Nietzsche's Superman prevailed; and where human beings followed nature's merciless way in which the lion ate the lamb.

In modern terms this implied selective breeding to create a Super Race; the weeding out and destruction of the weak or imperfect; the conquering of 'inferior nations' to ensure *Lebensraum* [21] and the 'elimination of Oriental pollution from foreign bodies', particularly the Jews. Elimination, eradication, liquidation, termination, final solution – all would come to mean the one thing – *genocide.*

NUREMBERG, Germany. 15 September, 1935. It was here, at the annual Nazi Party Rally on this date, that the central Nazi theories were institutionalised. In the Nuremberg Race Laws, German Jews were henceforth excluded from citizenship. They

---

[19] Papal audience of 22 April, 1935
[20] Literally, 'Belief in God'
[21] Living space

were also forbidden to marry or to have sexual relations with persons of 'German or related blood'. To do so was declared racial infamy, and became a criminal offense.

Jews also lost their right to vote, and were deprived of almost all political rights. Even people with Jewish grandparents, who had converted to Christianity, were defined as Jews. Even Germans who hadn't practiced Judaism for years found themselves caught in the grip of Nazi terror.

The following month came 'The Law for the Protection of the Hereditary Health of the German People'. Those wishing to marry had now to obtain from the public health authorities a certificate of fitness to marry. Such certificates were to be refused to anyone attempting marriage in violation of the Nuremberg Laws, and also to anyone suffering from hereditary illness or contagious diseases.

Another month later, on 15 November, the laws were extended to forbid marriage or sexual relations between people who might produce 'racially suspect' offspring. This was to include relations between Germans and black people, and also Roma (gypsies), or their offspring.

VOGELSTANG, bei Mannheim, Germany. 2 December, 1935. It was a conference for beginning mission workers. Franz Reinisch's words, however, did not begin with references to overseas, but to the Homeland.

'As I went for a walk last evening,' he began, 'I passed one of those lovely wayside crosses that stand outside so many of our villages, and that speak so beautifully of our Christian life and heritage. There were offerings of flowers beside the cross, symbols of piety, love and devotion. The birds were singing as if there were no tomorrow, and the winter sun was surprisingly warm. It was a little haven of peace.'

Franz paused. 'However, right beside the cross stood a large black-and-white sign that no one could possibly miss. It read: *Juden sind hier nicht erwünscht.*' [22]

There was an anxious stirring among the young listeners.

'My dear friends, we are gathered here to promote the world mission. That cross by the wayside is the symbol of the world mission, the symbol of truth and freedom. And thus also of the world's redemption. The Jesus on that cross is the world's apostle, who lived and bled for all the world. For *all* the world, I say. He died for all, *and that includes the Jews.*'

'Were you out of your *mind*, Father?' The Vogelstang pastor was beside himself. 'Do you realise the trouble you could get us into, here? There were spies in that chapel, you can be damn sure of that.'

'So what did you expect me to say? Was I to keep my mouth shut on – on the madness that's going on around us? Why haven't *you* spoken out about that sign?' Franz was nearly as angry as the pastor.

'They're at every crossroads, Father. Which you well know. And you come swanning in here to make trouble for us. Go preach your Jew-loving somewhere else.' The pastor stood up. 'I'd like you to leave tonight, Father. We'll cancel the rest of the conference. You're only going to cause us trouble, and God knows we have enough here as it is.'

---

[22] 'Jews not wanted here.'

16

Many men carry their conscience like a drawn sword, cutting this way and
that, in the world, but sheathe it, and keep it very soft and quiet,
when it is turned within, thinking that a sword should not
be allowed to cut its own scabbard
Henry Ward Beecher

DUSSELDORF, Rhineland-Westphalia, Germany. December, 1935. When the city's Youth House, headquarters of the Catholic Young Men's Association, was closed and sealed, and the clerical and lay organizers arrested, it was only one small instance of the icy grip of Hitler tightening on Protestant and Catholic organizations throughout Germany.

In the years to follow, that grip was to get tighter until it reached strangulation point. Clergy and lay leaders of all denominations would be targeted, with thousands of arrests over the years. Smaller religious minorities such as the Seventh Day Adventists and Bahá'í Faith would be banned or simply disappear. Jehovah Witnesses would be executed. Protestant leaders like Dietrich Bonhoeffer would first be imprisoned and then murdered.

Franz Reinisch watched appalled, as the Concordat with Rome was routinely flouted, as youth leader Baldur von Schirach forbade the simultaneous membership of church youth organizations and the Hitler Youth, and then made membership of the Hitler Youth compulsory on all. It even reached a point where a local Area Leader simply declared the Concordat null and void:

> 1. In accordance with the district order of April 25, all Catholic Youth and Young Men's Associations are forthwith forbidden in the interests of public peace and order and for the protection of the State and its citizens.

> 2. The above order renders void the protection granted with reservations to the said associations under the terms of Article 31 of the Reich Concordat of July 20, 1933, between the Holy See and the Third Reich. [23]

'Their aim is to get the children,' Franz said in a lecture around this time. 'The Nazi revolution is the greatest blow to Germany that has ever taken place. It is a blow to all Christianity. The state is claiming not only the bodies of our people but their souls.

'Force, not goodness, is the measure of all things. They want the children so they can replace Christianity with their own mad religion.

---

[23] *Mainfränkische Zeitung*, 25 April, 1934

'As the bishops have said in their combined pastoral from Fulda, "It is no longer a question of attacking individual dogmas or beliefs as in former religious conflicts, but it is the whole essence and basis of Christianity which must be overthrown. In carrying out their war of annihilation [the Nazis] are agreed that it is principally against Rome and The Roman Catholic Faith that their attacks must be directed..."'

HOHENRECHBERG, Schwäbisch-Gmünd, Germany. February 1936. The ruins of the great castle still tower above the village, having survived attack in the Peasant War of 1525, the Thirty Years' War and the French Revolution, finally to succumb to lightning in 1865.

In its shadow stands the little pilgrimage church of *Marienheiligtum* [24] with its image of 'the Beautiful Mary', an image believed miraculous. A regular pilgrimage to the shrine goes back to at least the 14th century.

It is to this pilgrimage church, and its parish of 700 souls, that Franz Reinisch was now assigned.

His first problem was with the Swabian dialect, difficult for a man from the Tyrol. There were misunderstandings, some of them quite comic. Even after months he still got things wrong. On one occasion he was inviting a group of local girls to an afternoon retreat. One said she couldn't come, as she had to go to her *Öhmden.*

'Well, can't you visit him later?' Franz suggested, as usual not taking *No* for an answer.

---

[24] Also known as 'Mary Help of Christians'

The young one had to explain that the word didn't mean fiancé but the second cutting of the hay. There was considerable mirth among the girls at that.

Another problem was Franz's increasing dependence on cigarettes. Over and over in his life he had tried to quit, but had never succeeded. It bothered Sister Gundhildis, housekeeper at the parish residence, which was also a hostel for pilgrims. Finally she took him to task: 'So much smoking, Father. That's just not right. The last father here only smoked three times a week.'

Years later she recounted: 'Like a poor sinner he stood before me and said: "That's true, Sister. I'm a bad so-and-so. I'll quit right now." Of course he didn't, but he certainly did cut down a bit.'

He also switched from *Heer & Flotte* to *Nordland* cigarettes, maintaining, without the slightest justification, that their darker tobacco was 'healthier'.

Franz was bothered by the fact that no priest had come out of that community for hundreds of years. 'For a place of pilgrimage there's a strange lack of spirituality here,' he observed.

He set out to try and deepen it, through confraternities, mission days, lectures and prayer groups, the establishment of a little Schönstatt company, and devotion to Mary during the month of May. Soon quite a few of the young people were turning to him for guidance. It is significant that four of them later entered the Schönstatt community at Vallendar.

When October came he held devotions each evening with a sermon. Every day the congregation grew, until by the end of the month it included most of the folk of the village.

Franz continued to set great store on prayer, and spent much time in the little pilgrimage church of Hohenrechberg. In a note at that time he wrote: 'God often wills that the soul can find no way out and must go through an impenetrable darkness. When one is in such a situation it is a good idea to mentally or physically kneel before the tabernacle and, with the Lord in Gethsemane, say, Thy Will be Done.'

There was darkness even in this remote valley. Even here Franz found himself under the eyes of the Gestapo, as all Austrians were being watched since the murder of Dollfuss. Attitudes to Austria were tinged with suspicion. To cross the border cost 1,000 marks. As an Austrian, Franz could not give school lessons.

It helped for the moment that the burgomaster of the region was well disposed to him, and spoke favourably of him to the Gestapo. For the moment, anyhow.

But the outside world was darkening and Franz was painfully aware of it. When a local weekly paper made an ugly attack against priests and the sacraments, Franz was heard to say: 'So, it's good. We must be persecuted to death, if we want to live according to the Lord. It's all perfectly clear: and it will get worse.'

Get worse it certainly did, in that dreary year of 1936.

On 7 March Adolf Hitler made his first move towards war, and gave the world its first sample of Blitzkrieg. In *Operation*

Schulung – 'the surprise blow at lightning speed' – three battalions of the Wehrmacht, using mostly horse-drawn transport, marched unopposed into Aachen, Trier and Saarbrücken, thus recovering the Rhineland from France, which had held it since the end of World War One. Neither France nor Britain intervened. On 27 July Hitler's Condor Legion began support for Franco in Spain, bringing the likelihood of a Europe-wide war ever closer.

It was at that time that Franz made his long-remembered remark to Sister Gundhildis. The good sister had always been worried that 'the two-storey father' would bump his head off the top of the doorway to his bedroom. That's what she called Franz because of his height.

'Don't you worry, Sister,' was the reply. 'If it comes to war, long Franzl will be shortened by a head.' And then, when he saw her distress, hastened to add, 'It's all right, Sister. That won't happen. All they'll do is shoot me!'

Of course not everyone saw 1936 as a year of darkness. Unemployment in Germany had been practically wiped out in the three years since Hitler came to power. The *Kraft durch Freude* [25] campaign brought summer camps and Baltic cruises for ordinary folk. Cinemas and dance halls were full; there was a radio in every home; and there was the dazzling spectacle of the Olympic Games in Berlin. There was even talk of a 'people's car' for every family – a *Wagen* for the *Volk, or Volkswagen.*

There was of course the shadow side, too, with the loss of civil rights; dissolution of the political parties; repression of the Jews; the ubiquitous presence of the Gestapo and the SS;

---

[25] Strength Through Joy

persecution of the churches; the closure of religious-order schools; the suppression of bishops' pastorals; nursing sisters expelled from hospitals and orphanages; another concentration camp opening, this time at Sachsenhausen, with news of more to follow. But it all seemed a price worth paying and, in the 'election' of 29 March 1936, the people backed Hitler with a vote of 98.9 per cent.

Later in the year came the October Protocols, creating an axis between Nazi Germany and Mussolini's Fascist Italy – an agreement which isolated Austria and left it ever more vulnerable, although no one seemed to notice.

But Franz Reinisch did.

In November came the Anti-Comintern Pact, creating an alliance between Germany and Japan. And in a sermon on New Year's Eve Cardinal Faulhaber, Archbishop of Munich, summed up the effect on the churches of that momentous year:

> Propaganda has been set on foot, whose aim it is with all possible resources, and by means of economic pressure, to de-Christianise the life off our nation, and to drive as many as possible to leave the Church. This propaganda is applied particularly to officials and those holding leading positions in the movement, together with those whose professions or occupations are economically dependent thereon. The hour has come of which Christ spoke: Satan hath desired to have you that he may sift you like wheat. [Luke 22, 31]

17

Give me the liberty to know, to utter, and to argue freely
according to conscience, above all liberties
John Milton

BRUCHSAL, Baden, Germany. 14 August, 1936. Once more a transfer for Franz Reinisch, this time to a dreary provincial town on the Saalbach tributary of the Rhine, renowned mostly for its asparagus. It had long seemed to Franz that as soon as he began to achieve anything worthwhile anywhere, he was invariably transferred somewhere else. 'Whenever I am settled anywhere, I must soon head off,' he complained to a Schönstatt colleague. 'Half a year anywhere, and I'm completely nowhere.'

At a farewell party the young folks of Hohenrechberg presented Franz with an umbrella and a poem of appreciation. A girl asked him to try the umbrella to see if it was big enough. Jauntily he opened it and a dozen cigarette packets fell out. They were much appreciated, as Franz's urge to smoke was greater than ever.

The transfer to Bruchsal brought a confrontation with the provincial superior, Josef Frank. It began with a postcard which an angry Franz sent, when he got word of his impending reassignment. The postcard was brief: 'Dear Father – Just why?'

By return post came the reply postcard, equally brief: 'Dear Father – Why not?'

That was too much for Franz, and he took the first train to Friedberg. Provincial Josef Frank received him coldly.

'Just where do I belong, Father?' was Franz's opening gambit. 'I don't seem to have a home any more. Where is my home, Father?'

'Have you any idea, Father, of the grief you are causing us all?' Josef Frank had his own agenda, and he was going to press it. 'You have a loose mouth, the biggest in the province, and have simply no idea, none whatsoever, of the problems you're creating for us. Why don't you simply shut up and get on with your work?'

'And what *is* my work, Father?'

'To preach the Word of God. Surely you know that.'

'And doesn't the Word of God include speaking out? What does Ezekiel say: *If the watchman doesn't blow the trumpet, and a sword takes a person, I'll require his blood from the watchman's hand* ? For God's sake, Josef, we've got to speak out.'

'Calm now, Franz. Just calm down. Let me explain a couple of things. Are you aware the Gestapo are on your case? – we've had hints of that. Several times. Actually I don't know why they haven't arrested you – I suppose they want us to get you to back off –'

'You mean, do their job for them?'

'It's not that simple.' The provincial leaned back in his chair and put his hands together. 'Look, Franz, none of this is going to last forever. Thing is, to keep our heads down until these people are gone. Not rock the boat – preach spirituality and holiness in the meantime. That's what all the churches are doing – trying to reach an accommodation with the regime. That's what the Concordat was about. We can't expect to do better than that.'

'And you know bloody well, Josef, the Nazis are breaking every agreement in the Concordat. Some are even saying it's invalid.'

'Franz, listen to me. Please. If I'd left you where you were, the Gestapo would have come after you, sooner rather than later. We even got a tip off from Rechberg. That's why I moved you on. It'll take a while for them to catch up.' He sighed. 'Look, I'm simply trying to keep one step ahead of them – keep *you* one step ahead. It's as simple as that. Please Franz. Accept it. There's no other way. And go easy, will you?'

In fact, there was another way, and it worked for a while anyhow. This was to assign Franz to give retreats to young men's associations and Schönstatt groups throughout Germany.

It became a sort of roving commission which meant that, although nominally based in Bruchsal, Franz was mostly on the move.

As he put it himself in a letter to the Schönstatt group in Hohenrechberg, 'Now it's about going through town and country, to announce to people Christ the Saviour of the world. I bring you all with me, asking you to strive and struggle invisibly through prayer and sacrifice.

'For a priest needs a great army of prayer for his task. And how calming it is for him to know that behind him praying hands join together, to help mediate God's blessings to other souls. O lovely Rechberg, the blessed hill of Mary, with your many simple and joyful children in God, with your powerful torrents of grace and your fruits of blessing.'

Soon enough, however, Franz was made aware of a decree from police headquarters in Munich:

> We have been informed that of late a striking number of regular priests, notably Jesuits, move from place to place as itinerant preachers. Special attention must be given to them, more particularly to the missioners. Observations are to be handed in at once with carefully-checked particulars of the individual and depositions of witnesses for any sermon preached.[26]

From then on Franz's preaching itinerary avoided the region around Munich. It was around this time that he came to Oldenburg, at the invitation of Bishop Graf von Galen of Münster.

---

[26] The *Persecution of the Catholic Church in the Third Reich*, p.109

OLDENBURG, Lower Saxony. 4 November, 1936. Franz Reinisch had just finished a lecture to senior students when a couple of workmen came in, carrying a large framed picture of the Führer.

When they then proceeded to remove the crucifix from the wall above the dais, Franz was less than pleased, to put it mildly: 'Who the hell do you think you are, and what do you think you're doing?'

The men shrugged. 'Just doing what we're told, Reverend,' one said. 'Haven't you heard the decree?' They then lifted Adolf Hitler up on the wall to take the place of the crucifix.

The men were correct: a decree that very morning from the area's Minister for Churches and Schools had ordained that 'in future ecclesiastical and religious symbols – e.g., the crucifix or the picture of Martin Luther – or any of a similar character, are not to be affixed to any building belonging to the State, communities or rural district authorities. Such as are already affixed are to be removed.' [27]

And of course there was already a nationwide decree that the picture of the Führer should everywhere be accorded 'its rightful place'. Zealous local authorities were now falling over themselves to remove the crucifix from schools.

'And replace it with Germany's new god, is that it?' Franz Reinisch stormed off to see Canon Vorwerk, who hadn't yet heard of the decree. He wasn't pleased either, and neither was Bishop von Galen when he got to hear of it.

There was uproar in the whole diocese of Münster, with a mass meeting in the city square in front of the ministry on 24

---

[27] *Münster Diocesan Gazette*, Supplement No. 51

November. The minister tried to calm the excitement by saying that the crucifix might be put up during religious instruction.

But the uproar continued and grew.

Finally the regional Gauleiter had to declare: 'A wise government must ever be able to reverse decisions that may have been wrongly made. The ordinance of 4 November is rescinded. The crosses shall remain in the schools.'

At a thanksgiving service the Bishop of Münster, Graf von Galen, declared:

> Let us thank God that he has opened our eyes and enabled us to recognize what an unholy development was taking place here in our midst, and what immeasurable evils stood before us... You did recognize it. From nearly every parish brave German men, tried and tested both in war and peace, have journeyed to Oldenburg, and, casting aside the fear of men, have given witness for you and for your loyalty to Christ. The cross shall remain.
>
> And if it should be our lot for the sake of the Cross to suffer shame and persecution with Christ crucified, then we shall neither fear nor shrink. For then we shall think of Him, who, himself dying on the cross, yet won for us the victory of life eternal.

Franz had by then returned to Bruchsal, but was heartened to learn that similar demonstrations were taking place all over Germany. Not all succeeded but many did, such as in Trier, Bislich and Emmerich.

Franz Reinisch, sometime after his ordination to the Priesthood at Brixen-im-Thale, Tyrol 29 June, 1928.

Photo courtesy Franz Reinisch Forum, Schönstatt

The story that Franz relished most came out of Palling, near Traunstein, in nearby Bavaria. There the local mayor had had the crucifix removed from above the classroom dais, and replaced it with the Führer's picture. The crucifix, deemed foreign to the Germanic nature and an oriental product of Judaism, was banished to the back wall.

However a crowd of extremely angry and rather burly local farmers paid a call on the mayor, who instantly agreed to reverse the situation, replacing the cross to its accustomed place and evicting the Führer back to the back wall.

18

If I look into my conscience I see but one law, relentlessly commanding:
to lock myself into myself and in one stretch to act
of my sacrifice and my obedience
Ranier Maria Rilke

BRUCHSAL, Baden, Germany. 2 January, 1937. The growing menace of Naziism came even more forcibly home to Franz Reinisch when the Gestapo arrested his rector in the Paulusheim in Bruchsal. There was simply a banging on the front door at 3 a.m. and, by the time Franz and a couple of others tumbled out of bed and reached the door, the rector, Father Hans Schäfer, was being bundled into a car at the bottom of the steps.

Where he was taken no one could find out. Franz, now temporarily in charge, protested loudly, even from the pulpit. The response was a deathly silence.

Even the battles over the crucifix turned out to be pyrrhic victories. Mostly the authorities simply waited until the furore died down, and then quietly removed the crucifixes and put

Hitler back where he belonged. Or where they believed he belonged.

'What will become of these crosses?' asked Bishop Sträter of Aachen. 'These are the crosses upon which Christian parents have gazed in piety and joy, which a long line of your Christian forbears have venerated and loved. What will become of them, now collected together and taken off in truckloads?'

As the Nazis grew in power they redoubled their onslaught on all but their own mad faith. In their determination to eliminate what they called 'the poison of Nazareth', their methods ranged from subtle to brutal.

It included easing non-believing teachers into religious schools with the task of undermining the children's beliefs; the firing of 600 teaching nuns in Bavaria; dismissal of state employees whose children were not being brought up as Nazis; forbidding the sign of the Cross and the Our Father, as happened for example in a community school of 500 Catholic and 35 Protestant children, in Neumarkt, Oberpfalz, in October 1937.

Adolf Hitler was gradually taking the place of God. Or of his Messiah at least. He had declared in *Mein Kampf* that world peace could not arrive until 'that day when a man superior to all others will have conquered and subjugated the world'.

Hitler of course was that man, and his Nazis were now presenting him as a god or as our mediator before God. 'Adolf Hitler, yesterday, today and the same forever,' was chanted by the Hitler Youth on the feast of St Boniface. Robert Ley: 'We believe on this earth in Adolf Hitler alone.' Julius Streicher, publisher of *Der Stürmer*: 'It is only on one or two exceptional points that Christ and Hitler stand comparably. For Hitler is far too big a man to be compared with one so petty.' The Mayor of Hamburg: 'We can communicate directly to God through Adolf Hitler.' Reich Propaganda Minister Josef Goebbels: 'Germany has been transformed into a great house of the Lord, where the Führer as our mediator stands before the throne of God. Everything the Führer utters is religion in the highest sense.'

'A lie limping through the land,' was Franz Reinisch's sardonic comment on this – a not very tasteful reference to Goebbels's club foot.

There was even a new version of the Lord's Prayer, to be recited by the Hitler Youth:

> Adolf Hitler, thou art our great Führer. Thy name makes the enemy tremble. Thy Third Reich comes; thy will alone is law upon the earth. Let us hear daily thy voice, and order us by thy leadership, for we will obey to the end, even with our lives. We praise thee; heil Hitler, Führer my Führer, given me by God. Protect and preserve my life for long. You saved Germany in time of need; I thank you for my daily bread; be with me for a long time, do not leave me, Führer my Führer, my faith, my light – heil, my Führer.[28]

[28] Robertson & Zimmerman.
www.cbn.com/700club/features/churchhistory/godandhitler/EZ15_god_a nd_hitler.aspx

Franz was especially grieved at the ever-mounting attacks on the Virgin Mary. There was a particularly vicious attack in an issue of the *Durchbruch:*

> There are still mothers who kneel before the Madonna's altars, blinded by the glimmer of candles and the gilded glitter of paint to the murky gloom which lies behind the plaster. Future generations, however, will not bow in the dust before a 'spotless Mother', nor will they attribute their sinfulness to the Original Sin of mankind.
>
> We Nordic men now oppose the glistening shield of our honour like a firm wall against that Jewish orientalism which would trample the honour of German womanhood in the dirt. Our clarion call rings out for the defense of German womanhood, and we ignore all attempts to wash it away with Catholic or Protestant baptismal waters.[29]

Like a flash from heaven, came a new transfer for Franz Reinisch, this time back to Austria. To Salzburg, once more. It was from the pulpit here that he uttered the memorable words, 'Satan is loose in Germany. I know. I've been there, and I've seen it.'

On 3 February, came yet another reassignment, this time to the provincial house of the Pallottines in Friedberg. Germany again. Probably so they could keep an eye on him, Franz suspected, and he may well have been right. These

---

[29] *Durchbruch,* Issue No. 10, 1936

assignments are making me dizzy,' was his comment. 'But perhaps it's as well. I seem to wreck anything I ever start – maybe because I set my demands too high.'

BRUCHSAL, Baden, Germany. 10 March, 1937. Franz was once again based at the Paulusheim here, when *Mit Brennender Sorge* crackled over Germany like thunder. In this encyclical Pope Pius XI finally took Hitler to task. The text had to be smuggled into Germany in total secrecy. Almost 300,000 copies were then printed, and read at masses throughout Germany on the following Palm Sunday, one of the busiest of the year.

The encyclical said it all. Written in German instead of Latin, so as to go straight to the people, it condemned the blatant breaches of the Concordat that had continued unabated since 1933; it excoriated the myths of Blood and Soil, and the making idols of race, state or nation. 'Man, as a person, possesses rights from God,' the encyclical said, 'and those rights must be protected against denial, suppression or neglect.'

> Where We tried to sow the seed of a sincere peace [the encyclical read], other men – the 'enemy' of Holy Scripture – sowed it over with the cockle of distrust, unrest, hatred, defamation... They, and they alone with their accomplices, silent or vociferous, are today responsible, should the storm of religious war, instead of the rainbow of peace, blacken the German skies...

129

Whoever follows that so-called pre-Christian Germanic conception of substituting a dark and impersonal destiny for the personal God, denies thereby the Wisdom and Providence of God. Whoever exalts race, or the people, or the state... to an idolatrous level... is far from the true faith in God and from the concept of life which that faith upholds...

None but superficial minds could stumble into concepts of a national God, of a national religion; or attempt to lock within the frontiers of a single people, within the narrow limits of a single race, God, the Creator of the universe, King and Legislator of all nations before whose immensity they are 'as a drop of a bucket'.

There was reference to 'a mad prophet', but neither Hitler nor his Nazis were actually named.

There was no need to, and Hitler had a fit of carpet-biting that confined him to barracks for three days.[30] The SS and the Gestapo confiscated all the copies they could find, shut twelve presses throughout Germany that had dared print the document, and suppressed magazines that had run the story.

The full fury of the regime was experienced at the Bruchsal house, when the Gestapo raided it and spent two whole days ransacking it. Franz was lucky to be absent at the time, for on

---

[30] *Teppichfresser* (carpet-eater) was Hitler's nickname among foreign journalists in Berlin. In times of fury he was said to throw himself on the floor and chew the edge of the carpet. (*Adolf Hitler*, by Patrick Delaforce, page 148)

his return he had to face a badly-wrecked presbytery and Paulusheim, that took many months to repair.

However he was even more fortunate to be back near Oldenburg at the time, to witness what happened when seven young girls were arrested for having distributed the encyclical after he had finished the Sunday mass.

Once more the spirit of the Oldenburg folks did them credit. A large crowd gathered in front of the Essen parish house where the Gestapo had taken the girls for questioning.

'Give us back our girls!' the crowd yelled. 'We want our girls! We want them now.' The chant grew louder: 'Now! *Now!* We want out girls! We want our girls! We want them *now!*"

The situation was growing ugly, and a policeman tried to fetch a car to take the girls away, but the crowd prevented it. Another police car was summoned from Oldenburg, but the crowd would not let it through.

A very scared Mayor then said he would let the girls go.

The crowd refused to believe him: 'None of your tricks,' they shouted. 'We heard that before.'

There was a tense standoff until about 7 p.m.

Then the police suddenly just marched away, and the girls appeared in the doorway to the wild enthusiasm of the crowd. They went off in a group to the church, and all of a sudden the church bells began to ring.

And so it all ended peacefully: the crowd slowly dispersed, and the girls remained free.

During that year Franz Reinisch had the almost permanent feeling that his life, or perhaps the life of Germany, was

131

running out of control. It seemed as if the Nazis were determined to revenge themselves for the insult of the papal encyclical.

Catholic journals and newspapers were shut down; priests arrested and sent to concentration camps; monks put on trial for currency smuggling and immorality; further seminaries and training colleges closed. As a Reich Education official expressed it at the University of Munich: 'I was delighted – I say again, delighted – to wipe twenty monkish training colleges off the face of the earth with one stroke of the pen. I say, nevertheless, that was but a beginning...'

Matters were made even worse with the worldwide report of criticisms uttered on 18 May at a diocesan conference by Chicago's Cardinal Mundelein. It was close to the bone when the cardinal asked how a nation of 66 million intelligent people 'could submit in fear and servitude to an alien – an Austrian paperhanger, and a darn poor one at that, I am told...' The speech then touched on things unmentionable in Germany:

> Perhaps we would understand if we lived in a
> country where every second person is a government
> spy, where armed forces come in and seize private
> books and papers without court procedure; where
> the father can no longer discipline his boy for fear
> the latter will inform on him and land him in prison;
> where personal savings and treasured securities are
> seized and sold to increase the gold supply.
>
> Perhaps we would understand if we lived in a
> country where letters are opened and read, as in
> wartime they do only with enemy correspondence;

where the young, tenderly nurtured girl is torn from the mother's side and sent into labour camps to live with the slatterns of the street; where the candidates for the religious life are not only sent into the work camps but into the military camps as well.[31]

There was outrage in Germany, especially when American Protestant churches expressed approval of the cardinal's words. Of course the speech never saw print in Germany but was surreptitiously circulated after being picked up on world radio. The *Hamburger Familienblatt* trumpeted an article entitled 'American Churches Unite for Hate Agitation.' It did not, however, quote the cardinal's actual words.

In July of 1937 one further concentration camp was opened. It was at a place called Buchenwald (which translates pleasantly as 'Beechwood').

---

[31] *Chicago Tribune,* 19 May, 1937. 'Mundelein rips into Hitler for Church attacks'

19

Their faces were contorted with a horror only known to
those who have silenced their consciences
Chris Nicolaisen

BRUCHSAL, Baden, Germany. 15 June, 1937. It seemed sometimes as if Franz Reinisch was in a race against time. There was a sort of urgency in the retreat lectures he gave at this time. And there was the constant awareness that there might be Gestapo spies among his audiences.

At one lecture he quoted a 1925 utterance of Pius XI, that the greatest and most urgent of all works is the work of the missions. And for that, he said, we must all be supporters. It's not primarily financial support, nor is it a matter of momentary enthusiasm, but a lasting healthy attitude to mission work.

'Today it is a matter of doing the ordinary things extraordinary well, as Sainte Thérèse always reminded us,' he said. 'A blessed apostolate can only flow from a true inner spirit. All other works are empty and void.'

Every listener understood the reproach against those in power: 'People far from God, and in hatred of God, may do sensational and earth-shaking things, but their works are dead before God. They make stories, but not history.'

Franz stared down at a young fellow in the audience who was taking notes. There was a long pause. 'Why don't you tell that to your masters, Gregor? They might like to hear it. Go on, now. Get out of here!'

The embarrassed young man stood up, hesitated, then headed for the door.

'What thou hast to do, do quickly,' Franz called after him. Then he turned to his listeners with a wan smile: 'Can anyone remember, brothers, who was the first ever to hear those words?'

'Judas,' came the answer.

INNSBRUCK, Austria. 5 March, 1938. Franz Reinisch was on a visit to his hometown, and was sharing a *Stiegel* beer with his old school-friend Anton Loidl. They were sitting in Café Krill on Hofgasse. Loidl was off duty so he wasn't wearing his police uniform, but one of those grey Tyrolean jackets with green lapels. The men were discussing the hyped-up tension between Austria and Germany.

'I'd have no trouble uniting with Germany, Anton,' Franz was saying. 'I mean, we were all one in the Holy Roman Empire. We were a federation together after Napoleon. We had a customs union in the last century. For heaven's sake, we're all German speaking. It's that bloody Versailles that's pushed us apart.'

'And so it's time we united again, surely?' Loidl put down his beer and leaned forward. 'Isn't that what Hitler keeps saying?'

'*He's* the problem, Anton. He's the very reason we can't unite. Imagine that criminal taking over Austria. It'd be the end of the world. Listen, I know. I live there. You've no idea what it's like. There's no way we could unite while that brown shit is in power.'

Loidl was silent. He quietly sipped his beer.

'Say something, Anton. You don't agree?'

Anton Loidl gently pulled back the green lapel of his jacket. Nestled there was a small white circular badge edged with red. In the centre was a neat little black swastika.

INNSBRUCK, Austria. 1.14 p.m. 12 March, 1938. The voice was Goebbels, but the message was Hitler's. It was the rasping vowels of the Reich Propaganda Minister that came over the wireless, but it was a speech of Adolf Hitler he was reading:

'This morning soldiers of the German armed forces have been crossing all of the German-Austrian borders. Armored units, infantry divisions and SS units on the ground, and the German Luftwaffe in the skies... will ensure that the Austrian People are given the opportunity to determine for themselves their future, and thus their fate...'

The Reinisch family sat in silence around the little wireless set as the sound rose and fell in the crackling ether. Franz Reinisch, on a visit home to his family, was holding his mother's hand. His married sister sat head in hands. Papa Reinisch just stared ahead. There was a glint of tears in his eyes.

'I myself, as Führer and Chancellor of the German People,' the rant continued, 'will be happy once again to be able to enter the country which is also my homeland as a German and a free citizen.

'The world, however, shall see for itself that, for the German People in Austria, these days are filled with hours of blissful joy and deep emotion. They regard their brothers who have come to their aid as saviours who have rescued them from great distress! Long live the National Socialist German Reich! Long live National Socialist German Austria!'

Franz could hardly speak. 'Is Austria come to this?' he managed to say. 'They've stolen it. Dollfuss murdered. Now this. Our land in the hands of criminals. Brutality without par.'

VIENNA, Austria. 2.48 p.m., 14 March, 1938. Franz Reinisch was sitting over a beer with his father on the terrace of the Café Central, on the corner where Herrengasse and Strauchgasse meet. The sky was blue and there was an unexpected touch of spring in the air. People were sitting out, almost for the first time since winter. Still, most were well wrapped up.

It had been a long-anticipated trip to the capital for father and son, and they had decided to take it in spite of the events of the previous two days. They were both still deeply distressed.

High above them monstrous red-white-and-black swastika banners swung down gently in the breeze, hanging from almost every balcony.

'Where did those all come from, Papa?' Franz said to his father. 'I mean, how did they get so many flags in time?'

'They knew it was coming, Franzl. They've known it for a long time, believe you me. I've known it. We all did.'

'But did they want it? I mean, this is Austria.'

'I'm afraid, Franzl, quite a lot did want it. *Do* want it. And the rest are scared to speak out.'

'Same as back in Germany, then. Hey, what about poor Schuschnigg? Did he know it was coming?'

'Of course he knew. Well, after what Hitler put him through at Berchtesgaden, he'd have been a fool not to know. And, in fairness, he did all in his power to stop Hitler.'

'Any news, Papa, of what's happened him? He hasn't been heard of since – since all this began.'

During the previous half-hour, almost without the two men noticing, the street had begun to fill with people, until finally they were packed metres deep on either side of the street. Brown uniforms seemed suddenly everywhere.

From far away there came the sigh of what seemed like a distant wind. The sound came ever-so-slowly closer, and gradually louder, until it became the mesmerising chant of *Sieg Heil! Sieg Heil! Sieg HEIL! Sieg HEIL! SIEG HEIL!* **SIEG HEIL! SIEG HEIL!** [32]

It grew and grew to become a mighty roar, and then suddenly arms were stretched upwards in salute, and then everyone at the café tables was standing erect with outstretched arm. Well, almost everyone – a few remained sitting. Among whom were the Reinischs, father and son.

The roar suddenly became deafening, mingling with the multiple growl of passing engines, and then, above the heads of

---

[32] Hail Victory

the crowd, there was the momentary glimpse of the top of a brown uniform and an arm curled up and back in acceptance of adulation.

'Well, fancy that, then! Finally I've seen him,' Franz leaned back and chuckled. 'The shit-brown Führer himself.'

'Franzl! *Franzl!* Would you keep your voice *down!* For God's *sake!'*

The smell of motor exhausts mingled with the underarm odour of thousands of outstretched arms. Then, as the roar of engines faded down the street, the fading chant seemed to change. It was more rhythmic now, and the words had morphed into *Ein Volk, Ein Reich, Ein Führer. Ein Volk, Ein Reich, Ein Führer...*[33]

UNTERMERZBACH, Bavaria. 23 May, 1938. If Franz Reinisch loathed any place, it was that novitiate where he had suffered such depression, where the novice master had taken away his cigarettes, and from which he had tried to run away until he had heard the word *stay.* And now he was back here. Worse still, he himself was now the novice master.

He didn't like it one bit, and depression came back with a vengeance. It wasn't cigarettes this time, because he could smoke as much as he liked. And did.

It helped that Hitler hated smoking, and that the Nazis were at the time conducting a campaign against what they called *Passivrauchen* [passive smoking]. Hitler's hostility made smoking even more pleasurable.

---

[33] One People; One Reich; One Leader

Franz's constant smoking, however, irritated some of his brethren, especially when he puffed away non-stop during meetings and at recreation. During one after-lunch recreation Father Stanislaus tossed a copy of *Reine Luft* [Clean Air] across the table to him. 'Take a peep at that, Franz,' he suggested. 'Know what they've just discovered? That if a woman smokes too much it comes out in her milk.'

Franz stood up and it looked as if he would hit him with the magazine. 'I'm not a fuckin' woman, Stan!' he roared. 'Or haven't you noticed?'

And then, when everyone started to laugh, he ended up laughing himself.

The depression, however, seemed here to stay, and sometimes thoughts of just walking out, quitting the whole thing, came back to haunt. At such times he spent hours in prayer, to what he called his MTA – his 'Mother Thrice Admirable'.

It seems that the interminable shifting and reassignments were getting to Franz. Whether or not they were keeping him ahead of the Gestapo – which was doubtful – they were awaking in him deep feelings of homelessness and insecurity.

'I feel like a beggar,' he was heard to say. 'Without a place I can call home.'

His mood was not helped by ominous political developments. When the Munich Agreement of 29 September was announced, where the European powers simply sold out and allowed Hitler to occupy the Sudetenland, Franz was aghast. When this was added to the fact that Hitler had by now made himself supreme commander of the army after sacking generals Fritsch and Blomberg, the outlook was bleak.

'First Austria, now the Czechs – there'll be no stopping him now,' was Franz's comment. 'We'll soon have a shit-brown Europe!'

Also the wait-and-see attitude of some of the brethren towards the Schönstatt movement, so dear to Franz, was getting to him. At times it seemed to amount to hostility.

'What is it, Franz?' Father Stanislaus found him sitting one day on the garden seat near the little white-washed shrine. He was watching a couple of chaffinches busy on the lawn.

'Ach, it's nothing, Stan. Just – it's what we all go through. You know, from time to time.'

'It's more than that, Brother. I've been watching you. Come on. Out with it. Tell old Stan.'

There were tears in Franz's eyes. 'Y'see that wall, Stan? The tumbledown bit over there? When I was here first, years ago, I nearly climbed that to get out of here.'

'Would you do it again?'

A snort. 'I wouldn't go over the wall. It'd be the front door this time!'

'Tell me something, Franzl. Tell me straight, now. Where would you really like to be?'

'Schönstatt. I can think of nowhere else.'

20

SCHÖNSTATT, Rhineland-Palatinate, Germany. 26 October, 1938. Franz Reinisch was forever convinced that Stanislaus had gone behind his back to Josef Kentenich, to get him transferred to Schönstatt. Which was probably true. Well, if so, he was profoundly grateful.

This was where Franz belonged. He had always known it. There was the sheer physical beauty of Schönstatt, set in the glorious landscape where the Rhine and Moselle meet, with their highlands of the Westerwald, Eifel and Hunsrueck.

But for Franz this simply mirrored what he perceived as the far greater beauty of the spiritual world into which he now entered. Whereas in some of the order's houses there might have been doubts about what seemed excessive or exaggerated devotion to the Virgin Mary, here it flourished and Franz thrived in it.

In the grounds of the monastery there still stands a tiny ivy-covered chapel that contains, above the altar, a world-famous portrait of Our Lady of Schönstatt, here honoured as 'The Mother Thrice Admirable' – or MTA. In a diary, kept later in prison, Franz wrote how this little grace chapel became for him 'a homestead, a place of healing and a place of achievement'.

It was a place, he said, where he spent hours daily in prayer, 'growing in security in matters of faith, and clarity in thought and desire'. There he gave thanks 'for the love that here surrounds me', and asked pardon for his reserve, sensitivity and 'coldness in offering love. For it is only now here in prison that I realise what warmth surrounded me in that community.'

In the diary Franz is particularly thankful for the spiritual security he found in Schönstatt 'on account of the supernatural air of the whole family – priests, sisters, family members, and finally on account of the shrine and its secrets.'

It was of course a daily struggle for a man of Franz's temperament: 'I stood like a wanderer on the edge and strand of the sea of grace that surged back and forth. Well did I try to swim, and also to cruise – that is, I tried to practise the daily order.

'A powerful and hard school, it's a school of suffering, in which the MTA now leads me. But only such a school could still have an influence on my character. So I will only thank her from my heart.'

The 'father' of Schönstatt was Josef Kentenich, the Pallottine who had actually founded the movement in 1914. His continued presence here had a profound effect on Franz Reinisch, who found the man's genial personality 'on the one hand a radiant example, on the other hand a constant reproach'.

As he said later: 'I suffered a lot in Schönstatt under Father Kentenich, because I had the feeling he completely saw through me. If something was not right, then he said something to me indirectly, so that I felt myself completely seen through. His spiritual and mental attitude made his constant presence almost unbearable. Yet I never had such a yearning for another person as for him.'

The two men talked a lot about conscience, especially as the Nazis kept telling people to put conscience aside and simply leave it to the Führer. It was becoming daily more clear to Franz that everything he himself was doing, the stand he was taking against the Nazis, the things he said in his lectures, mostly boiled down to following conscience. And he had the foreboding that conscience would soon be demanding more of him.

But what exactly was this conscience thing?

'It seems to me,' Franz said to Kentenich, as they walked together in the sunlit garden by the chapel, 'it seems to me like some kind of little box inside your head that flashes red or green when you're deciding something.' He paused to light a Nordland. 'And if you do the wrong thing it keeps on flashing red, and gives you an awful time. God, I ought to know!'

'They call that guilt, Franz. Or remorse. We've all had it. From time to time, anyhow.'

145

'I'll tell you something, though, Father – the one thing I've always remembered is my Papa's advice. That it's not about big or small, but right or wrong.'

'He was certainly spot-on there, Franz. Actually, I see conscience as a sort of three-step spiritual process. Say, there's something we know naturally – like, it's wrong to steal. But then our reason applies it to a particular instance – if I took this purse it would be stealing. And the third step is – well then, I won't take it. That's why we call it *con-scientia* – Latin for "with science". We're applying our knowledge to a particular case. It's as simple as that.'

The pair turned at the Calvary at the end of the garden.

'So what's Hitler at, then?' Franz pulled at his cigarette. 'Telling us that *he's* our conscience?'

'He's pinched that from the military – remember, he was in the war. And much of Germany's been militaristic since Fredrick the Great. The first thing they do in the military is stop the soldiers thinking for themselves. Make them like a machine. Remember that English poet Tennyson: Theirs not to reason why – theirs to do or die. Otherwise they'd never go over the top.'

'So Hitler's at the same game – I can see that now. He even has the Hitler Youth convinced their duty is simply to die for the Führer. But how do you counter that?'

'Conscience must be absolute – the ultimate arbiter. That's the only answer. It is the very last thing we have, and we must follow it no matter what.'

'So what if the bishops tell me something I can't accept?'

146

'They can inform – that's their duty. But they can't decide for you. Of course your conscience must be properly informed so that you make the right decision. And they can help there, so we do need to listen to them.'

'And then decide?'

'And then decide.'

'So, tell me then, Father, why are so many people following that bastard Hitler, then? Surely they have consciences? I mean –'

'It may be hard for you to take, Franz, but some truly believe in him – quite a lot do, actually. People like that have badly informed consciences, but it's not easy to blame them because of the constant lies and propaganda. That Goebbels is a genius, don't forget.'

'An evil genius.'

'You can say that again. Then there are others who ignore their consciences for what they can get out of it. And of course if you ignore your conscience often enough and long enough, it dies. You then simply have no conscience – no thought of right or wrong, or of anyone but yourself. In other words, you become what they now call a psychopath.'

'Like those top Nazis? I think a lot have become like that.'

'They weren't always, Franz. Some probably started with the best of intentions – but once you close your eyes to evil, you become part of it. It's downwards from there on.

'But the vast majority of folks, I'm convinced, are just too scared to follow their conscience. They're the ones that pretend not to notice, when they see Jews being beaten up on the street. They just want a quiet life. Actually sometimes I think

147

the whole of Germany is like the three Japanese monkeys – see no evil; hear no evil; speak no evil. But remember the fear here is absolutely hideous. And it's everywhere, as you well know. You have to live here to realise it. The thought of Dachau can pop many a conscience into the back pocket.'

'Not all, Josef, thank God. Maybe there's only a few, but I saw people take a stand in Oldenburg when the Encyclical came out. I've had hope ever since then.'

'Hold on to that hope, Franzl. It's all we have now.'

VALLENDAR, Rhineland-Palatinate, Germany. 10 November, 1938. When Franz Reinisch cycled into nearby Vallendar to get his weekly supply of Nordland cigarettes, he found a strangely tense atmosphere in the streets. Brown uniforms seemed to be everywhere, and there was broken glass on the pavements.

When he reached his usual outlet, Zigarrenhaus-Goldberg on Goethestrasse, he found a huge white six-pointed star daubed on the front window.

A storm trooper stood outside the entrance. 'I wouldn't go in there, Reverend, if I were you,' the man said to Franz.

Franz brushed past him into the shop, where he found old Goldberg sitting weeping on the back stairs. His tiny wife sat with her arms around him.

''What the devil's going on, Abe?' Franz demanded.

As if in answer, there was a crash and the front window disintegrated as a massive concrete block hurtled through and landed on the counter. Shards of glass flew everywhere, clinking among the empty tobacco tins that were scattered across the floor.

Old Goldberg got a fit of shaking and Franz thought he was witnessing a heart attack.

'Abe, Abe. What is it? What's going on?'

'There's no cigarettes, Father. They took them all.'

It was only in the days that followed that the people at Schönstatt realized the full extent of what had been happening. Some idiot, apparently, had shot a German diplomat in Paris. It was extremely convenient to the regime that the assassin happened to be Jewish, which gave Goebbels the pretext to attack Jewish businesses throughout Germany.

In a two-day pogrom of arson, looting, and mass murder, conducted by Storm Troopers, SS, and ordinary citizens, while the police looked on, more than 1,000 synagogues were burnt, 7,000 Jewish businesses wrecked, hundreds of Jewish people killed and more injured, with 30,000 arrested and taken to concentration camps. In later years they were to refer to it as *Kristallnacht* – 'The Night of the Broken Glass'.

When Franz went back a day later to check on Abe and his wife, he found little more than a gaping hole where the shop had been. There was no sign of the old couple, and no amount of enquiries could elicit any information, beyond that neighbours had seen them being taken away.

'Where is it all going to end?' Franz said to Josef Kentenich when he returned. 'Or maybe I should be asking, where am I going to end? I mean, I've got to take a stand, somehow. I can't be one of those Japanese monkeys.'

21

In matters of conscience, the law of
the majority has no place
Mahatma Gandhi

SCHÖNSTATT, Rhineland-Palatinate, Germany. 10 February, 1939. It was a mystery to Franz Reinisch that he had not yet been lifted by the Gestapo. With Schönstatt as a base he was crisscrossing Germany, giving retreats and conferences, especially aiming at binding together and confirming the hopes of the little groups who had developed from Schönstatt.

Due to the tensions in the country, and the machinations of the Nazis, there was a noticeable decrease in the whole Christian lay movement throughout Germany. Schönstatt was no exception. Franz now concentrated on gathering together small elite groups of people who understood the developments of the time, and could foresee their consequences.

This could easily have been interpreted as treasonable activity, and perhaps it was so interpreted. But Franz seemed to have a charmed life. He knew it wouldn't last, so made the most of it while he could.

From the industrial regions of the Rhine and the Ruhr, through Swabia, Bavaria, and Westphalia, he set out to equip the young men and women for what must come.

'In this unchristian, indeed anti-God atmosphere of the present,' he said to one group, 'we have to trust the church to individual believers. You, brothers and sisters, have to become witnesses, apostles of the truth. *Indeed, you must become lay priests.*'

This was strong stuff, but it seemed the only way. Franz saw exactly that anyone who practised genuine Christianity under Nazi rule, must do so alone.

'You must,' he told his listeners, maintain your place out of your own responsibility and inner decision of conscience. *And this often in complete isolation.*'

The message was both fearful and harsh, but to speak otherwise would have been dishonest.

At another retreat he told his listeners: 'Only a man or woman filled with the deepest conviction of Faith, equipped with the strength of grace from the Holy Spirit, sealed with the cross of Christ, could and can, individually and alone, be an insuperable opponent against all the clutches of the new paganism.'

FRIEDBERG, near Augsburg, Germany. 15 April, 1939. It was only a matter of time before Franz Reinisch was once more summoned before his provincial superior.

The waxed-floor smell was as strong as ever, and Josef Frank was as bothered as ever. The Gestapo had come calling again. 'Do you really want to see Dachau, Father?' he asked.

'Mind if I smoke, Father?'

'Oh, for God's *sake*, Franz! Oh well, do as you please. You will, anyway.'

'Thanks, Father.' Franz paused to light up, and offered a cigarette to his superior, which was abruptly declined.

'I don't understand why they haven't picked me up by now,' Franz went on. 'Father Kentenich seems to think I have a charmed life.'

'That's all very well, Franz. But it's not helping us. We have to live with these people – don't you understand? They're shutting seminaries and churches all over the place. Could you at least curb your language? I mean, the way you refer to the Nazis?'

'Well, von Galen calls them "the Browns". I just go one step further – I call them "the Shit Browns"!'

'That's what I mean, Franz. There's no need for language like that. It just makes enemies.'

'They're already our enemies, Father. Surely you know that.'

'Look, couldn't you just keep off troublesome topics – touchy subjects. And show a little respect. You know what I mean.'

'Respect for those criminals, Father? You must be joking. And you want me to preach those bland sermons they're all at? Vague, uncommitted, pathetic stuff? Pussyfooting around? What you hear in every church? Up and down the country? Holy purity and all that? Holy obedience to – to our lawful rulers? Oh, for God's sake – is that what you want?'

Frank sighed. 'Now that you mention it, Franz – I could order *you* under Holy Obedience –'

153

'You're forgetting, Father, there's one thing beyond Holy Obedience.'

'And what's that?'

'Conscience.'

SCHÖNSTATT, Rhineland-Palatinate, Germany. 16 April, 1939. Franz Reinisch was more upset by his provincial than he cared to admit. He had cooled down by the time he got back to Vallendar, and the bit about Holy Obedience was bothering him.

'Am I wrong, Father?' he asked Josef Kentenich, as the pair strolled between the shrine and the Calvary at the end of the garden.

'Perhaps you could keep the brethren a bit more in mind,' Kentenich suggested. 'Josef Frank had a point there. I think, perhaps, the essence of what you're saying is fine. But you might couch it in more diplomatic terms. You *are* a bit hasty – you know that, Franz, don't you?'

'I suppose I do. Maybe this charmed-life thing is going to my head. I'm kind of taunting them. Why haven't they lifted me?'

'Have you ever considered, Franz, that we here at Schönstatt are a mirror image of the Nazis? We too demand loyalty and total dedication of every single person – not to Hitler but to Christ and his Mother. And we're vying with Naziism for a spiritual renewal of Germany – in different ways: they want their mad pagan religion; we want Christianity.'

'So what's that to do with it?'

154

'In a way they see us as fanatics like themselves. And you're one of the worst. That's a compliment, by the way. In their eyes.'

A blackbird was tapping on the lawn nearby, and the pair stopped for a moment to watch. The bird cocked its head sideways, listening for the worm.

'You're a bit like him,' Kentenich said. 'Knocking to see whom you can bother. But I'll tell you something, Franz. I do have a theory why they're leaving you alone. As I said, you're a fanatic.'

'What do you mean?'

'You're a fanatic, Franz. Face it. Not so different from the Nazis in that. And in their own perverse way they respect that. If you ever flipped, if you ever came over to them, you'd be worth your weight in gold.'

'You must be joking. You know me better than that.'

'I do. But *they* don't. Remember there was a priest joined the SS lately – it was trumpeted in all the papers. Fanatics do flip – I mean, look at Saint Paul – fanatical persecutor of the Christians, and then – pouf, Damascus. Maybe you could have a reverse Damascus.'

'You're having me on, Father. That's –'

'Of course I am, Franz. I'm only teasing you. You're as immovable as those Tyrol mountains you go on about – just as long as you curb that pride of yours, which could be your undoing. And as long as you keep up those prayers to the MTA.'

155

VALLENDAR, Rhineland-Palatinate. 20 April, 1939. It was the Führer's birthday when the summons came. Gestapo HQ, the Marienburg, Heerstrasse 52, was where Franz Reinisch was required to present himself.

It was like a doctor's waiting room: smallish hall full of silent, apprehensive people. But no children bouncing around. And no magazines to read. A silent black-clad figure standing against the wall, booted feet apart – now *he* wouldn't have been in a doctor's waiting room. Everyone here with eyes to the ground. Scent of unwashed bodies. Or perhaps just sweat? Hint of one's own sweat too. Frisson of anxiety through the room whenever that door opened at the far end. Another black uniform, barking out a name: '*Reinisch! Franz Reinisch!*'

A walk down a long corridor with a hand on your left shoulder. Jackboots clacking beside you on the tiles. Smell now of carbolic. A whimper from behind some door. Another door opening. Bare bleak room. Chair to sit. Two men across a table. Both in civvies. One in leather coat – bald, square head, fiftyish, neck pushing against collar.

The interrogation was unexpectedly mild. Papers were shuffled, notebooks opened. Did you say this? Yes. Did you say that? Yes. And that? No. And this? Yes. *Why?*

'Because I believed it to be right.'

'But perhaps not opportune, Padre?'

'Would it ever be opportune, with you lot around?'

Leather coat creaked as the interrogator leaned back in his chair, pushing the notes aside, putting fingers together. 'Why don't you come over to us, Padre? We could do with a fellow like you. Think it over, will you?'

'*Steuermann, Steuermann trink mit uns.*'

'Huh?'

'Ach, nothing. You wouldn't understand.'

22

Idolatry, like all sin, is devastating to the soul.
It cuts us off from the comforts of grace,
the peace of conscience, and the joy
that is to be our strength
Elyse M. Fitzpatrick

SCHÖNSTATT, Rhineland-Palatinate, Germany. 28 April, 1939. The late daffodils that spring were lovely as ever, their yellow trumpets still silently summoning the world to wonder at their peacefulness.

As he walked among them in the monastery garden, Franz Reinisch realised that little else in that fearful spring was silent or peaceful. Hitler was roaring his head off in Berlin, and that very day had revoked the German Non-Aggression Pact with Poland. While the daffodils trembled in the breeze, the world trembled in apprehension of what was to come.

Spring is usually seen as a time of hope, but in that spring of 1939 there was the sense of a Europe accelerating towards some kind of Armageddon. In his mad *Drang nach Osten,*[34]

---

[34] Drive to the East

Hitler had already taken over the remainder of Czechoslovakia (16 March), proclaiming the Protectorate of Bohemia from Prague Castle. Poland was now to give back Danzig, and President Roosevelt's offer of mediation was rejected. On 28 April Germany renounced the naval pact that had been signed with Britain. On 21 May the 'Pact of Steel' was signed, strengthening the axis between Fascist Italy and Nazi Germany.

And finally, on 23 August, came the most fateful pact of all, when Nazi Germany unbelievably signed a non-aggression agreement with Communist Russia. This Molotov-Ribbentrop Pact was the death-knell of Poland and the last step towards war.

The persecution of the churches continued unabated. The 'Jewish-oriental origin of Christian morality' was constantly mocked and attacked. Reinisch was appalled when a young trainee teacher passed him a just-issued booklet that accused Christianity of 'a scorn for life and for all life's values'. Teutons don't believe in a personal God, some Nazi Dr. Siegler was proclaiming:

> The idea of perpetually waiting and listening for salvation... is typically oriental. Such an attitude is responsible for oriental teachings about revelation and personal conversion. It is the key to those hallucinations which mark the history of churches and sects. The concept of salvation and revelation constitute the grand self-deception of all Orientals.

Germanic morality, the good doctor claimed, is determined solely 'by obedience to the eternal laws of life, and has but one motto, namely – the strongest must be victors, *and the victors must rule.'*

'But that's the law of the jungle,' a furious Franz said at a confraternity meeting. 'The absolutely lowest form of jungle life. It makes us simply animals, hideous creatures – monsters that tear each other to pieces because one is bigger than another. And that's exactly what's happening here in Germany – no, in the whole of Europe now. Nowhere, no one, is safe anymore.'

Franz was particularly distressed by the seduction of Germany's young people. 'When I think of the children and the youth, my heart cries out,' he said at the time. 'That they are made to worship other than Christ.'

Indeed the personal cult of Hitler, as he ploughed towards Armageddon, was more and more clearly taking on a religious drive: with mass events that were more than ever like religious services. There were altars to Hitler in many houses; consecration of banners by the Führer; Eucharistic processions where the swastika replaced the Sacred Host inside the monstrance. There were even prayers to the Führer in the schoolbooks. Prayers like this:

> Führer, my Führer, given me by God,
> May you long guard and receive my life!
> Thou hast rescued Germany from deepest need!
>
> I thank you today for my daily bread.
> Remain long by my side, leave me not,
> Führer, my Führer, my Faith my Light.
> Heil, my Führer!

Confiscations of church institutes continued unabated. The Missions Institute of St Ruprecht in Kreutzberg was dissolved and taken over by the Salzburg school foundation. This, as the local Gauleiter said, was 'to render innocuous a rallying point of anti-German opinion'. The ancient abbeys of Göttweig, Admont, St Lamprecht and Engelzell were confiscated by the Nazis.

A visiting Swiss citizen reported as follows on the closing of the Servite Monastery in Innsbruck:

> After a thorough search had been made, all the members of the Order were ordered to the front hall near the door, where they all had to stand with their faces against the wall. They were informed that they would have to leave the house within three-quarters of an hour, and that they would be allowed to take small articles with them (in a small handbag)... They were then freed one by one at lengthy intervals of time...

> While the Fathers were being evicted... rifles and machine-guns were loaded into trucks drawn up at the monastery porch, in order to make it appear as if weapons had been found in the monastery. These are the facts and I can vouch for their accuracy. I am a Swiss.[35]

A hostel run by the Sisters of the Holy Cross in Feldkirch bei Klagenfurt was confiscated by order of the Gestapo. It was declared state property for having lent its aid 'to endeavours hostile to the State and people.'

---

[35] Persecution of Catholic Church in Third Reich, p 47

The Catholic hospital in Duisburg was closed by order of the local chief of police. Because of closures throughout the country, teaching and nursing nuns were deprived of all means of gaining a livelihood. A report by the editor of *Commonweal* in the US estimated that at least 15,000 nuns in Germany were without home or sustenance.[36]

Sometimes it seemed as if Christianity itself was imploding. Newspapers had been gleefully reporting trials of priests for seduction of the young, and for currency smuggling.

From everywhere came statistics of desertions and apostasies from Christianity: in Vienna alone, in the six weeks from the annexation to 24 April, 6,000 a week were leaving the Catholic Church. There were even printed apostasy-declaration forms being distributed, and many people simply lacked the courage to refuse the signature demanded.

It was particularly difficult for anyone in state employment: word came that more than 2,000 police in Vienna alone had yielded to the pressure from above.[37] Franz wondered about his friend Anton Loidl, although there was no information about the Innsbruck police.

In a conference at the time, Franz mingled despair and hope:

> About the figure of Christ there is a constant coming and going. The steady falling away from the Church speaks to us in accents of woe: men on whom we thought we could count forsake the company of Christ. Yet others there are who are

---

[36] Persecution of Catholic Church in Third Reich, p. 48
[37] Ditto, p. 232

coming over to Him, men of whom, but yesterday, we could not have believed it possible. No one dares foretell today what the morrow will be.

It is true we mourn each soul that turns its back on Christ – for each is our brother signed with the blood of Christ – but we can still say, broadly, that one who today cleaves to Christ is worth ten who have stood by Him through mere force of habit and have forsaken Him at the first alarm. There are many, too (we need only refer to the statistics), who spend but a short time in the chill darkness of separation from Christ and, let the door open ever so slightly, are straightway back within their Father's house.

Almost every Easter Franz Reinisch had the custom of visiting the little old-world town of Lügde, to take part in the beautiful Holy Week services there. The ceremonies end with the ancient custom of the Easter Wheels.

As night falls on Easter Saturday, the Easter Fire is lit beneath the cross on the *Osterberg* [Easter Mountain] and then giant blazing wooden wheels, their spokes plaited with oil-soaked straw, are rolled down the mountainside, while the congregation sings the hymns of the Resurrection.

On this Easter Saturday afternoon of 1939 Franz arrived on the train from Hamelin. He was dismayed to find the railway station swarming with black SS uniforms and the brown and black of the Hitler Youth.

'What on earth's going on?' he asked Sister Amalia, who had come to meet him.

'You might as well take the next train back, Father. They've told us to stay out of it. The SS have taken the whole thing over.'

'God almighty, has it come to this? Well, I'm staying.'

'Father, you can't take part. There's no place for any of us up there tonight.'

'I'll be up there, Sister. At least I can watch. And maybe pray a bit.'

'Well, at least don't wear your cassock, Father. That could be dangerous – you know how people can get worked up.'

'But they're our people, Sister.'

The sister sighed. 'It's different, now, Father. People here have changed, I'm afraid. They're not like they used to be.'

The ceremony was dramatic as ever – but different. Franz Reinisch stood among the crowd in the darkness, in a dark overcoat and without his priest's collar. The night was chilly but clear. The stars hung high above and they were diamonds.

Franz watched the torchlight procession wind its way up the mountainside, the flames eerily illuminating those fervent but frightening young faces of the Hitler Youth. He listened as the mesmeric chant of the Horst Wessel Lied replaced that glorious Easter hymn, *Wir wollen alle frölich sein.* He listened as the choir of the local BDM[38] sang *Es zittern die morschen Knochen:*

> The rotten bones are trembling,
> Of the World before the War.

---

[38] *Bund Deutscher Mädel* – the League of German Maidens

We've smashed this awful terror,
And victory's in our power.

And marching we'll continue,
Tho' all else breaks apart;
For Deutschland's heart beats in us,
And next the whole World's heart

Franz listened as the local Gauleiter bellowed his oration, not about the Risen Lord but about the Rising Sun. He listened to the rhythmic chant of *Sieg Heil! Sieg Heil! Sieg Heil!* as it reverberated across the valley. He watched the giant blazing wheels tumble down the mountainside – as the sun tumbles down the sky – but tumbling now, not for the Risen Christ, but for the shit-brown Führer.

And he wept.

For some reason this became for Franz Reinisch the symbol of all that had become horrible in Germany, and he returned again and again to it whenever he preached – how the great wheel of Christianity was being spun away from the people.

Franz's aim, as he criss-crossed Germany in that last year of peace (or rather, of non-war) was to strengthen his groups of young people in their determination not to be driven out of their thinking for themselves:

'Beware,' he kept repeating, 'beware of the synchronizing of hearts and minds, for that is how this land of ours will be undone.'

Every one of such conferences was most certainly spied upon, and could only be interpreted as a general attack on the

166

unlimited authority of party and Führer. Yet Franz remained untouched, and no one could say why.

It was almost a relief when war finally came.

23

GLEIWITZ, Upper Silesia, Germany, 31 August, 1939. Events began with an attack on a German radio station here – *Sender Gleiwitzin*. A contingent of German soldiers, dressed in Polish uniforms, staged the attack. Under the leadership of one Alfred Naujocks, they took over the station and broadcast an anti-German message in Polish. A concentration-camp prisoner had been dressed in Polish uniform, lethally injected, then shot and left for dead, to make for greater authenticity.

Thus was staged the pretext for World War Two, the war that Adolf Hitler had yearned to have in time for his 50th birthday. The next day German troops marched into Poland in *Operation Fall Weiß*, and on 17 September the Soviet Union took over its agreed share of Poland, in terms of the pact signed only a week before the German invasion – the Molotov-Ribbentrop Pact.

Three days later, on 3 September, honouring their pledge to Poland, Britain and France declared war on Germany.

Men turned pale all over Germany as they realised what this meant. Few believed the propaganda that this was England and France trying to encircle Germany. But they did believe what the 1935 Conscription Law meant. It meant they would soon be called to fight. The oath to Adolf Hitler was now a reality: all would be required to swear it.

'*And that I will not do,*' was Franz Reinisch's immediate reaction.

SCHÖNSTATT, Rhineland-Palatinate. 10 September, 1939. Franz Reinisch's stance on military service and the Hitler oath was not always appreciated within his religious community, in those days of trepidation after the outbreak of war. It certainly did not help that he trumpeted his views loudly and often, as was his wont in most matters about which he felt strongly. It helped even less after the joint pastoral from all of Germany's bishops in support of the war:

> In this decisive hour we encourage and admonish our Catholic soldiers, in obedience to the Führer, to do their duty and to be ready to sacrifice their whole person. We appeal to the faithful to join in ardent prayers that God's providence may lead this war to blessed success and peace for the Fatherland and People.[39]

---

[39] Guenter Lewy. *The Catholic Church and Nazi Germany*, p.226

This soon led to a flaming row in the priests' common room at after-supper recreation. The Saturday evening ration of schnapps made the flames flare somewhat higher.

'You'll all be called up, you know, sooner or later,' Franz was saying. 'And I'd guess sooner.'

'What d'y'mean, *we'll* be called up?' Father Heinrich demanded. 'What about you, Franz?'

'Oh, I'll be called, too, but I won't serve.'

'You'll have no option.'

'Yes, I will. I'll simply refuse to take the oath. And that'll be that.'

'It won't be just that. You'll be shot.'

Franz shrugged. 'Then so be it.'

'I'll tell you something, Franz. You won't be so tough when the time comes. Wait till you see. Besides which, the Pope's new encyclical says it's our duty to serve. *Gaudium et Spes* – it's quoted in today's paper.'

'Yes, typical. The bastards are quoting the encyclical to suit themselves. The devil can cite scripture to his purpose.'

'Let me get it for you, Franz. It's right here.' Heinrich grabbed the paper and read:

> 'All those who enter military service in loyalty to their country should look upon themselves as the custodians of the security and freedom of their fellow countrymen; and when they carry out their duty properly, they are contributing to the maintenance of peace.

'That's the Pope, Franz. What d'y'make of that?'

171

Franz was growing ominously steely, and the little group in the common room sat back to enjoy the confrontation.

'I'll tell you what I make of it, Father. It says contributing to maintaining peace, doesn't it? Let me ask you something – is trampling all over Poland, flattening Warsaw, maintaining peace? Come off it! And it says "loyalty to their country" doesn't it? But here it's loyalty to the shit-brown Führer, is it not? Isn't that how the new oath reads?'

'Pipe down, Franz. Look, I'm a historian, and I can tell you the early Christians even prayed for Nero and recognised him. What's the difference here?'

Franz was not moved. 'This bloody oath on the Nazi flag is the difference. Look — up to '34 the oath was to the Fatherland and the People. I'd have taken that oath. But now it's to Hitler personally, to a scoundrel – you cannot take it, and that's all about it. It would be sinful. You'd be giving an oath to a criminal.'

'It's an obligation in conscience –'

'Conscience my ass! I'll tell you something, Heinrich. Our conscience forbids us to follow an authority that brings only murder and death into the world. For their shameless conquering. *You cannot take an oath to a criminal.*' He turned to Kentenich. 'What do you say, Father Josef?'

Josef Kentenich had been following this verbal duel with interest. But he now stayed subtly out of it – or rather, he took the part of the individual conscience, more strongly than was customary in church circles at that time.

'Let each man see as it strikes him,' he said to the hotheads. 'Some things do not hold for everyone. If conscience tells you

172

one should take the oath, so then it is right. But if conscience rejects the oath, then one must follow the call of conscience.'

SCHÖNSTATT, Rhineland-Palatinate. 22 June, 1940. As Hitler's dreadful juggernaut rolled through Europe, grinding everything under its wheels, with Poland ruined, Norway falling and then France, Britain ousted at Dunkirk and bracing itself for a Nazi invasion, Franz Reinisch found himself more and more convinced of the righteousness of his stance on the military oath.

In one of his best-remembered lectures in the Schönstatt retreat house – remembered because it was so provocative – he cited Thomas Aquinas: 'His rules for a just war,' he said, 'are utterly concise. And unanswerable. First, a war must be fought on the orders of a legitimate authority. *Is this authority legitimate?* Secondly, it must have a just cause. *Where is the just cause here?* Thirdly, there must be a right intention – those fighting must intend either to increase the good or lessen the evil. *Is there such an intention here when it is all about brutal conquest and domination?'*

It was hardly a coincidence that the Gestapo closed the retreat house shortly afterwards.

As the war ground on, Franz felt himself more and more isolated in his stance on the oath. Sometimes it seemed that the whole Catholic Church was ranged against him. Rottenburg's Bishop Sproll had expressed the prayer that God might give the soldiers the strength 'to fight victoriously for the dear Fatherland or to die bravely'. (To which Franz replied, 'I would rather die for Christ than for Hitler.')

The Archbishop of Bamberg wrote that 'it is enough for a Christian to be obedient to the temporal authority and to draw the sword and fight true to his oath, against the injustice done to his Fatherland.'

Then the Catholic Military Bishop Rarkowski wrote in his pastoral: 'What these times demand in blood, sweat and tears, what the Führer and the highest authorities of the Wehrmacht demand of you soldiers, and what the Homeland expects – behind all stays God himself with his will and his command.'

Words such as these could leave Franz Reinisch at times close to despair. In this anguish he turned to his mentor.

'*Athanasius contra mundum,*' Josef Kentenich murmured. 'Remember poor old Athanasius? Against the world? When the world groaned in the Arian heresy, as St. Jerome put it, "God raised up one man to speak the truth." Maybe there's need for someone to speak the truth again.'

'But why does it have to be me, Father? I don't want the job!'

'You've already answered that, Franz. Conscience. You don't seem to have an option.'

'But why are all these bishops saying what they do? Don't they have consciences too?'

'Well, they keep coming back to Romans 13 – Let *every soul be subject to the governing authorities... and the authorities that exist are appointed by God –*'

'I know – *and whoever resists the authority will bring judgment on themselves.* Is that me, Father?'

'Conscience is the ultimate arbiter, Franz. And that's how God will judge.'

'But why –'

174

This is perhaps the best-known portrait of Franz Reinisch, likely taken during those final anguishing years leading to his decision to follow conscience as the ultimate arbiter.

Photo courtesy Franz Reinisch Forum, Schönstatt

'Let me explain something, Franz. What we're witnessing goes back a long way. All the way to Bismarck. Remember the *Kulturkampf* in the last century? Remember how Bismarck fomented the suspicion that Catholics were nationally unreliable? – that they had their command centre in Rome? Ultramontanes and all that? Well the bishops are terrified that the Nazis would start on that again – saying that Catholics are disloyal. Which indeed they *are* saying. So that's why the churchmen are shouting so loud about loyalty – they don't want to be outmatched by anyone. It's as simple as that.'

'But do they believe what they're saying?'

'I don't know, Franz. I really do not know. For their sakes, I hope they do.'

24

If all the world hated you and believed you wicked,
while your own conscience approved of you
and absolved you from guilt,
you would not be without
friends
Charlotte Brontë

FLORN-WINSELN, Baden-Württemberg, Germany. 13 June 1940. It was the last time that Franz Reinisch would ever be free to speak his mind publicly. Perhaps he felt it: in this lecture to fifty young men, he was forthright in his words.

'A basic law of the world,' he said, 'goes as follows. Evil usually has a natural victory over the good, but the good has the supernatural final victory.'

This, he said is proved in different periods of the world: 'Firstly, the serpent wins in Paradise. Secondly, in the Deluge, only a few are rescued. Thirdly, evil triumphed at the death of Christ. But only momentarily. And now here in Germany today, evil triumphs for the moment. The good are so often put down, so that evil triumphs. But finally comes the world Judge in the clouds of heaven.'

In the terrible situation of Europe today, Franz told his listeners, 'the only thing is to trust the church to individual believers, to equip them with godly strengths, to form them into witnesses, apostles of the truth, as lay priests, and so release them into the world.'

And these believers will be all on their own. 'There they must, often in complete isolation, maintain their place out of their own responsibility and inner decision of conscience.'

It's the values of the individual that makes the values of society, Franz emphasised. 'And society is only as good as the individuals that make up that society. If you want a proof of that, just look around you. A new sort of paganism everywhere.'

The New Paganism is the New Satan, and only faith can match it. 'And only a man filled with the deepest conviction of faith, equipped with the deepest strength of grace from the Holy Spirit, sealed with the cross of Christ, could and can individually and alone be an insuperable opponent against all the clutches of the New Paganism.'

Franz ended by quoting the words of his countryman, the Tyrolean poet Bruder Willram:

> We want men today in dull days
> Who carry high the holy banner of the cross,
> Despite hate and mockery in a strong bold hand;
> We want men without fear or hesitation,
> Who true to the faith strike the battles of God
> For our people, for our Fatherland

178

SCHÖNSTATT, Rhineland-Palatinate, Germany. 12 September, 1940, It has to come, and come it does. Whatever their hopes have been for Franz Reinisch, this is finally too much for the Gestapo.

Like a bolt from the blue, on the Feast of Mary's Name, comes word that the Gestapo in Berlin have placed on him what is known as a *Maulkorb* – a muzzle, a gagging order. From now on, Franz can no longer preach, hold retreats, lecture, even to the smallest of groups.

For Franz Reinisch, the rest is silence.

He is devastated. In the past, erring priests had been silenced by their church – but, by the Gestapo? The unthinkable has happened.

In a letter to a girl who had taken part in the retreat in Wuppertal, he wrote: 'I never guessed that these exercises would perhaps be the last ones for a long time. Perhaps you might let a few beads of the Rosary go through your praying hands for a priest who has been silenced. But be convinced that God's ways are always wonderful. *MHC – mater habebit curam* – the Mother will still care! With unshaken trust it goes ahead.'

At one point a spark of humour showed through, when he told a student he had been silenced for the next thousand years.

'How do you mean?' asked the student.

'Well, isn't this Third Reich to last for a thousand years?' was the reply.

179

It was when the *Volksempfänger* radio announced the execution of two members of the Jehovah Witnesses, for their refusal to take the military oath, that the full reality of his stand dawned on Franz Reinisch.

For the first time he realised – in the sense that it became real to him – the consequences of persisting in his stand. His thoughts lurched from admiration of the heroism of those two young men, so rare and so alone in Germany, to the sickening certainty that if he too refused the oath when the call-up came, *he – too – would – die.*

Nights became sleepless. Nights of endless tossing in bed; of wandering the monastery garden and even the local country lanes beneath the stars. Sitting head in hands, rocking back and forth. I don't have to. I don't have to do this. Maybe my brethren are right. *Conscience...?* But what about obedience? – my provincial...? Am I just hellishly stubborn? Is it satanic pride? *Conscience...?* Everyone else going along. I don't want to die. *I – don't – want – to – die.* I'd only have to sign and get it over with. Medical Corps then – hospital orderly, stretcher bearer. Could quietly work as a priest. Might even get to be chaplain. Could do so much good. *Conscience...?* Forget it, just this once. Would be so easy. I'd not have to die. And they'd all approve. Would even applaud. But – *conscience...?* Oh dear God, guide me. Show me your will. Mary, my mother, show me the way. Don't let me go astray. But don't let me die. *Conscience...?* Oh help me God. What is your will? Help me my Mother. MTA be with me now. I don't want to die, but... Oh help, HELP me God. Help me MTA... *Conscience...?*

180

Night after night after night after night. Day after day after day. Same two thoughts – *Don't-Want-To-Die* – and – *Conscience...?* Same two thoughts buzzing forever inside the skull, like two trapped wasps. Solar plexus throbbing. Eating ceasing. Bowels seizing – always a problem anyhow. Saliva drying. Headaches crashing, crushing. Ears buzzing. Tinnitus? Same two thoughts, round and round, inside the skull. As if it would burst. Oh Mother, oh MTA, *help – me – HELP – ME...*

Conscience...?

Suddenly then came the finish of Franz Reinisch's two-year sojourn at Schönstatt, centre of his world. Early in February the provincial sent him out of Germany altogether, to Bohemia, in the continued hope that this might help to evade the Gestapo, at least for another while.

It was a rather vain hope, as Bohemia was now a German protectorate.

25

I shall drink to the Pope, if you please,
still, to conscience first, and to
the Pope afterwards
John Henry Newman

AUSSERGEFILD, Bohemia. 9 February, 1941. Elves once danced through the streets of this little village, in Smetana's symphonic poem *Vitava*. But there was no dancing now under Nazi occupation. It had been called Kvilda until the Nazis came. Then they germanized it.

The village was sleeping under snow when Franz Reinisch arrived, this time to care for the inhabitants of the village, both German and Czech. He was to assist the parish priest, Father Eustachi. It was the loneliest assignment of all, but the shock of the move seemed to bring him some easing of his mental agony. Thirty centimetres of fresh snow on top of 75cm of old snow kept the snow ploughs forever active. The only connection to nearby Bavaria was a 10km pedestrian pathway.

'On-going stillness and loneliness' is how Franz described it in a letter. 'Air for retreat. And yet one doesn't grow holy any faster. We're a thousand metres high, cut off from the world, three quarters of a year of winter and cold. And the hearts here are just as cold.'

Understandable, perhaps, given that this was a German-occupied village.

AUSSERGEFILD, Bohemia. 1 March, 1941. 10.40 a.m. The postman delivered two letters that morning. One was a brief note from Anton Loidl to say that he had accepted a brilliant opportunity to join a special-duties police group in occupied Poland. The second envelope was graced with an eagle clutching a swastika. It was the standby order for entering the Wehrmacht. The call-up could be expected within a year, but could be any time. And nothing had changed: the call-up would mean certain death in the event of a refusal to take the military oath.

There are a couple of pages of diary preserved from this time:

Saturday, 1 March, 1941 –

Around 11 in the morning, while I was praying the breviary, I got from Schneider the standby order. I said nothing. I prayed more. Slowly it begins in me to sparkle and shine. The significance of this information is revealed bit by bit. Around 11.30 I go into the shrine. I met no one who could question me or enquire. I knelt before the All Holy...

There began a powerful spiritual struggle. What plan has Divine Providence for me? I have long had the feeling that I will not live much longer. And the manner of my death was clear to me. Has the time come? Is this the appointment with Christ the King?

184

A double urge drove me internally, to say yes to a freely chosen manner of death:

1. Commitment to the Marian kingdom of Christ, for homeland and family;

2. Flight from myself on account of my weaknesses and unreliability. The cruelty of death loses its power when one thinks of the daily insecurity, to be encountered in the homeland from bombs, but also on account of the completion of life, as an officer of Christ and Mary to die for a great undertaking, finally as an act of atonement for my poor sinful past life.

Now the question: is it God's will, that I choose this manner of death? What can give me the answer?

1. The past years of my life: Twice I was weak in decisive moments, when I believed myself to be strong enough. Could this coming thing be the third and last possibility? I know that without the strength and help of the Holy Spirit I will be weak again this time. Help, Holy Spirit, thou spirit of strength.

It's a matter of Christ's kingdom, for which I have been called through my ordination, as an officer to struggle and to die. Maria, my Mother, help me in this.

2. I am too weak to live a heroic priestly life. Also the thought: this is the easiest kind of death: it gives me a definite preference for it. I know well that there is a great difference between dying freely or forcibly. The thought that I can live longer if I choose otherwise is very tempting, if only out of self-preservation. And yet the wish to be a true priest and Schönstatt apostle makes the freely-chosen death more attractive.

185

3. Finally, through this death to fulfil an apostolate which I otherwise could hardly do better, makes it again more attractive.

For the Schönstatt kingdom. For the missions. For the people, above all for my Mother Mary. For the family and the children. For my hard-pressed Homeland. For the benefactors, for the conversion of sinners, for the poor souls, for the Holy Father, the bishops and priests!!!

Objection: there is no obligation to choose this death. Looked at in general, this may well be true. But here it's a matter of personal choice. I can use myself better for Faith and Fatherland through this manner of death. So I believe that God and his Mother expect it of me, and my Homeland too. Is this absoluteness and readiness not allotted to me by God? Yes.

O Death, where is thy sting? Every man must die sometime. As an officer of Christ I will victoriously return to the Father, victoriously bear witness to Christ the King... victoriously lose myself in the sea of love of the Holy Spirit.

He who loses his life will save it. The list of martyrs must first be made full. Do I feel myself called to be ready for that? Christ and Mary, give me clarity and firmness, the spirit of strength and love, but also the attitude of repentance and atonement! Let it come as always, I will be ready to fulfil the will of the Father. At the very least I will no longer live in the setting of total power....

Mother Mary, at the end I turn to you. Look at my past life. It was an up and down, a life and love in joy, but also a failure and escape. Look not on my sins and errors that I committed, especially as a priest, but on my struggle to belong just to you. And so I consecrate everything anew to you that I am and have, myself completely. And if it fulfils your plan, let me be a sacrifice for your work. Accept my strong belief: You will have victory over the times, and your work will never fail. Amen.

Yet it was still only the stand-by order. Much could happen in the meantime. And much did happen.

On 22 June, 1941, Germany invaded the Soviet Union. It was the largest military undertaking in world history. The aim of 'Operation Barbarossa' was the destruction of the Soviet Union, the seizure of land for German settlement (the *Drang nach Osten*[40]), the elimination of Communism, and the physical annihilation (i.e., mass slaughter) of all Jews, communists, and others deemed dangerous to German hegemony.

On 20 September, Franz got a letter from Schönstatt: the Gestapo had arrested Josef Kentenich, and no one knew where they had taken him. This was worse than any standby order. This man, spiritual father in everything to Reinisch, had now disappeared into what would be later called *Nacht und Nebel* [41] – that Night and Fog from which no one ever seemed to return. He would be *vernebelt* – 'turned into mist'.

---

[40] Drive to the East
[41] Literally, 'Night and Fog' – the Nazis took the term from a Tarnhelm spell in Wagner's music drama *Rheingold*

26

The torture of a bad conscience
is the hell of a living soul
John Calvin

ABENBERG, Roth bei Nuremberg, Bavaria, Germany. 15 October, 1941. When Franz Reinisch arrived in this little medieval town, which still looked almost as it had been in Wolfram von Eschenbach's *Parzival*, there was hope that he might be able to stay, as confessor to the sisters in the local convent.

Sometime after arriving in Abenberg, Franz is delighted to get a surprise visit from Anton Loidl. It means a great deal to him that his old comrade has taken the trouble to find where he is living and to seek him out.

The two men head for the open-air restaurant up at the Burg Abenberg. Some ersatz coffee and pumpernickel bread has to suffice. Rationing is getting tighter.

'And how are those special duties you've undertaken, Anton?' Franz wants to know. 'Going well?'

'It's really what I wanted to see you about, Franzl.'

189

'So tell me, old friend.'

There's a hesitation. 'I've – I've been killing people, Franzl.'

'But you're not a soldier, Anton. You're a policeman.'

'I'm a special kind of policeman, now, Franzl. I'm in an *Einsatzgruppe*. My job is shooting people.'

'What kind of people?'

'All kinds. Men, women and children. Well, Jews, mostly.'

The silence lasts a while. Franz just stares at his friend. 'Did I hear you right, Anton? *You've been killing people? You've been killing children?*'

'Them too, yeah. I have to kill all sorts. I've no option. It's my job, y'see.'

'What exactly do you do?'

'There's these big trenches – we have them already dug. Then we march the people out of the village to the trench, line them up, tell them to strip, and just shoot them. They fall straight into the trench. Then it's filled in – the engineers do that. That's all there is to it.'

'How exactly do you do the shooting?'

'We aim for the back of the neck. It's the surest. And it's more humane that way. We used to use machine guns but it was a bit haphazard – some would still be alive when the trench was filled in. And it was a shocking waste of ammunition.'

'So how do you feel about this, Anton?' Loidl hasn't noticed the steel that has crept into the priest's voice.

'It was hard at first, Franzl. I'd have to admit that. But you get used to it. Like in a slaughter-house, it'd be a bit unpleasant at the start. But you can get used to anything. Anyway, they're mostly only Jews.'

'Conscience, Anton?'

'No, that's OK. Y'see we're obeying orders. Besides, it's the Führer's will, and we have to work towards the Führer. Anyhow, in the end it's just a job. Like, we live quite normal lives: we've canteens; cinema; football matches at weekends – against the SS and the army; we've pretty well everything we need. Even home leave, like right now. Only thing is, we're not supposed to talk about – about our job. I could be in trouble just talking to you.'

'So why *are* you talking to me, Anton?'

'There's one thing's been bothering me, Franzl. There was this little blondie girl, about four, who wandered off without being noticed. When they'd shot everyone, the count was wrong – we keep careful records, y'see – well, I was sent to find her.

'I found her at the edge of the trees. She smiled up at me and took my hand. Like I was her papa, or her big brother. Well, I led her into the forest. And – and then, I showed her how to kneel. I had to show her, as I didn't speak her language. Then I showed her how to lie face down, with her face in the dry leaves. She thought it was great fun.

'Then I blew her head off. But – but bits of her brains and blood got stuck on my sleeve.'

The silence lasted longer this time.

'So what do you want from me, Anton?'

'I thought, maybe, you'd be able to give me, like, some sort of absolution. You know, as a priest, like. That little girl bothers me.'

191

"And for all the other killings?'

'Yeah, I suppose. Them too.'

'Are you going back there, Anton?'

'Oh yes, I have to. I'm just on leave. It'd be desertion if I didn't go back.'

'And you might be shot for that, eh? Wouldn't be nice, would it? Being shot, I mean. So you'd like absolution before you go back? For that little girl. Is that it?'

'I suppose so, yeah.'

'Did you ever hear of repentance, Anton? This is the Sacrament of Penance you're asking me for. It's not a fucking laundry – clean the bloodstains off your sleeve and send you back out to get bloody again. Bloody, did I say?' *Blood soaked would be more accurate.* You are soaked through with blood, Anton, right into your very soul. And the stench of it reeks to high heaven.' Franz stood up, knocking over his chair as he did so. 'You smell of hell, Anton Loidl. You're a child of Satan. *You – are – evil.* Like Cain, you're accursed on this earth. He only killed one – you've slaughtered hundreds – thousands by now. You are cursed beyond redemption.

'Get – out – of – my – sight! No, I'll get out of *yours,* because I can't breathe the stench that's coming off you. The stench of Satan. You reek of evil. I'm leaving now, and I won't even say Adieu, for that means God be with you.' He reaches into his soutane pocket, tosses a few coins on the table and stalks out, past tables of silent people.

ABENBERG, Roth bei Nuremberg, Bavaria, Germany. 16 October, 1941. 10.05 a.m. Sister Ancilla from the nearby convent is acting housekeeper at the presbytery. She taps on Franz Reinisch's door. 'A gentleman to see you, Father.'

When Franz sees Anton Loidl standing in the hall, he goes straight to the front door, holds it open, and roars, 'Get out! D'y'hear me, get out! *Get out!*'

'Franzl, aren't we friends?'

'Satan's your friend now. Get out of here.'

'I'm not going back, Franzl,' Loidl says.

'You *won't* get out?'

'No. I'm not going *back*. Back there.'

'Oho, deserting, are we? What will your beloved Führer say to that?'

'I'm volunteering for the Wehrmacht. Eastern front. I'm certain they'll take me – they need all they can get.' Loidl suddenly falls to his knees in the middle of the hall. 'Franzl, give me absolution, please. Please, I beg you, Franzl – '

'You're wasting your time, man. And mine. There could be no forgiveness for what you've done. Not ever. *Not ever.* It's too monstrous. Anyhow, absolution's a farce without repentance.'

'I do repent, Franzl. I've thought all night –'

'All those people rotting in those trenches, and you want a few words from me to wipe you clean? Is that it? You're making a farce out of the sacrament.'

'Franz. Don't you preach mercy? The mercy of God?'

'Mercy is it? What mercy did you show to those children? To their fathers or their mothers? There could never be mercy on earth or in heaven for the likes of you. After what you've done. Anton Loidl, you're beyond God's mercy...'

193

A gentle touch on Franz's sleeve. 'Father, isn't God's mercy infinite?' Sister Ancilla whispering. 'Don't you preach that?'

Franz turns, and his eyes are pools. Then he lurches towards the hall bench and throws himself down.

The tableau remains for what seems ages – the priest with head in hands; the mass-murderer on his knees in the middle of the floor; the silent sister standing by the kitchen door.

At last Franz gets slowly to his feet. 'Get up, Anton,' he says. 'Better come inside.'

After several months in Abenberg, it began to look as if Franz Reinisch's wanderings might have come to an end. He had made friends with the local pastor, Josef Sparer, a man of considerable influence in the town. The latter had high hopes of arguing that Franz's worsening health would now preclude military service, and was setting about persuading some local medical people to this end. He was also declaring Franz indispensable to the work of the parish.

Alas, it was not to be. The bishop of Eichstätt, in which diocese Abenberg is located, was aware of Franz's presence, and had been content with his ministry to the convent and parishioners. However, at a certain point he got to know of the man's troublesome reputation. Once he did, he wanted rid of him immediately.

'Get that fellow out of my diocese,' he ordered. 'And right away. I want no truck with the Gestapo.'

And so the wandering began again. But this time it was not to be for long.

27

Conscience is the magnet of the soul. It has a divine polarity. ... In the dark hours of trial, that only lie just this side of despair, then consult this Divine Monitor; though its tiny needle may tremble amid the attractions of earth, yet its polestar will be the throne of God

Horace Mann

PASSAU, Bavaria, Germany. 1 March, 1942. The final posting in the priestly life of Franz Reinisch would be to a village in the Passau diocese – a place called Wegscheid, as curate to the parish there with its onion-domed church.

It was almost an omen, for *Wegscheid* literally means a parting of the ways.

'And I'm at a crossroads,' he told his friend Pauline Englemeier when he stopped with her in Passau on his way to his new posting. 'Just you wait and see. I'm told the call-up is due any day now. But it'll be almost a relief when there's an end to all this wandering.'

He sighed and lit a cigarette. You know, Pauline, sometime I feel I'm like a beggar. Really just a beggar – a beggar that always has to eat at strange tables, like a hunted wild beast, that never finds rest.'

They were sitting at a table sharing the end of a bottle of *Dönnhoff Spätlese*. This gentle kindly widow, who was probably half in love with Franz, leaned across and took his hand in hers. 'There could still be hope, Franz. I know you've told me you'll never sign, and I've told you I've accepted that. Well, maybe you won't need to sign. There's always grounds for hope.'

'Well, at least I got some good news, Pauline. We know where Josef Kentenich is. We got word he's in Dachau. At least he's not dead. And do you know who's with him? Believe it or not, Kurt Schuschnigg. Imagine, the President of Austria in a concentration camp! But at least they're both alive.'

'See what I mean, Franz? There's always hope. Look at the possibilities, in your own case. I mean, look at all the illnesses you've had. And that chronic bowel trouble. The fact is you're unfit for military service. Genuinely unfit. And I'll tell you something – if you'll come over to the hospital here – where I work, y'know – they'll declare you unfit. I'd see to that – they're my friends there. But it would be an honest declaration, *because you're simply not fit.*'

'Do you really think there's hope, Pauline? I mean, Josef Kentenich always told me to sell my life as dearly as possible. I think he meant, not to force confrontation if there was a way out. Maybe you've given me a way. Oh Pauline, dear – I – don't – want – to – die.'

WEGESCHEID, Bavaria, Germany. 7 April, 1942. It was the Tuesday after Easter, but the postman was already back on his rounds. He touched his cap as he handed in the single letter to the priest. Franz's hand trembled as he took it. It was once more that green envelope that carried the eagle and swastika in the top left-hand corner. Same colour and official shape. It was clear what it contained. Franz stepped out from the doorway and vomited onto the grass.

Just one week – that's all there was left. The final call-up required Franz to report to the military barracks at Bad Kissingen on the following Tuesday, 14 April. Now it's *serious* – that was the only thought that reverberated around his head. Now it's serious – the rest had been playacting.

It had been far from playacting. The five weeks leading up to this moment had been a time of the greatest anguish Franz Reinisch had ever known, so that he sometimes thought of Christ in Gethsemane garden sweating drops of blood. And indeed his prayer was similar – *let this chalice pass.*

The struggle had taken many forms. Sometimes it was simply the thought of death itself. That all would simply end. But it doesn't end, does it? Oh Mother Mary, help me to remember that.

Other times it was the temptation of martyrdom. It's been so difficult, nearly impossible for me to lead a holy and heroic life, Franz told himself. Look at the smoking. The foul temper. The offence I've so often given. The cruelty I've shown. My pride and arrogance. I've been so weak and selfish. Maybe this one big sacrifice would achieve holiness in one fell swoop? One bullet, and straight into martyrdom.

Come off it – what a load of rubbish. Holiness on a plate? Subtlest temptation I've had yet. Get behind me, Satan.

The Germans and Austrians are great for wood-carved mottos, and there was one hanging at the top of the stairs in the presbytery where Franz was living. It read:

> A half sacrifice bleeds
> A total sacrifice blazes

Housekeeper Frau Fenzl often noticed Franz standing for ages in front of this carving. She would not have known that it was one of the favourite sayings of Father Josef Kentenich, and it may well have been the catalyst that triggered Franz's final decision. Whatever about that, when Pauline Englemeier came to visit on 29 March, she met a man who had made a final and irrevocable decision.

No, he wouldn't take the option of claiming ill health, even though he would be ever grateful to Pauline for the idea. No, he must make the stand against Hitler. Absolutely, without compromise: 'I've prayed every minute, Pauline, and struggled and fought for the right understanding. And no other understanding has come to me. So it must be right. I have simply no option.'

Now it's serious. It's one thing to accept the idea of dying, and quite another when death actually beckons. And death's forefinger was now curling. Little more than a week before being taken out and shot. *Now it's serious* – that's what those words actually meant. Death is a fearful thing, as Shakespeare once said.

Realising it can be even more fearful.

On the Wednesday, the day after the call-up had arrived, Frau Fenzl noticed Franz kneeling at the back of the church, during the school service. 'He had a scrap of paper in his hand, which he kept unfolding and reading, then folding again,' she said later. 'He wasn't erect as usual, but sort of bowed. It was like looking at the Lord on the Mount of Olives.'

Four days of leave-taking, and giving away most of his few possessions. God knows, there wasn't much to give.

'I won't be back, ever,' he told Frau Fenzl. 'The less you have, the freer you are.'

28

A man's conscience can tell him his situation better
than seven watchmen in a lofty tower
Ben Sira, *Sirach 37:14*

INNSBRUCK, Austria. 11 April, 1942. When Franz's married sister Hanni called to the parents' home she found an atmosphere of gloom. Which should never have been so, especially as her beloved brother was visiting. And the behaviour within the house was strange, to say the least.

'When I came into the room,' she said later, 'Papa and Franzl went into the kitchen. When I came there, then they went back to the living room. I thought it was pretty odd, as we never had secrets from each other.'

When Hanni followed them, she overheard Franz say, 'So Papa, did *you* give your vote to Hitler? Did you vote for the *Anschluss*?' [42]

'I certainly did not,' the father answered. 'What do you take me for?'

---

[42] *Anschluss* – literally 'connection' or 'annexation'. Word used for the 1938 incorporation of Austria into Nazi Germany's Third Reich.

'So what do you want from me, then? I'm your son. I won't give that bastard my approval either. You can't ask it of me.'

That was the end of that.

When later Franz went back to the kitchen, he found his mother cooking the dinner. 'Mutti, today you're preparing my last meal here,' he said to her.

'Why so, Franzl?'

He hesitated. 'Look, Mutti, it's – uh – I'll – I'll tell you later.'

The parents often prayed the open-air Stations of the Cross at the Tummelplatz Cemetery in the forest glade over by Ambras Castle. Franz and Hanni accompanied them there that afternoon: Franz thought it just might be an opportunity to explain to the mother what was about to happen.

But Hanni remembers that a great depression came down on him. By the seventh station he could not control his weeping. 'If it were only over,' she heard him whisper.

The mother heard it too. 'What is it, child?' she asked.

Franz could hardly speak. He pointed to Mary beneath the cross, and answered almost harshly: 'Look at her standing there. Well, so must you!'

When they came to the 13th station, Franz took his mother's hand: 'Mutti, can you also be a mother of sorrows? Can you carry your cross too, and not collapse under it?'

Slowly, quietly, came the answer: 'If God gives me the strength, then I can.'

'Mutti. Today I am with you for the last time. To say farewell to you, and to this world.'

'Are you ill, Franzl?'

'No, Mutti. But I *am* going to die.'

Then he told her.

INNSBRUCK, Austria. Hauptbahnhof, Südtiroler Platz. 14 April, 8.25 a.m. The train would leave in five minutes, so it was time for farewell. There was no weeping. The parents knelt on the platform for Franz to give them a final blessing.

'When you hear it is over with me,' he said, 'let there be no tears. Just pray a *Te Deum* and the *Magnificat,* and have no grief.' But there were tears in his eyes as he climbed into the carriage. As the train moved away and the parents receded into the distance, he leaned out and once more made the sign of the cross.

The mountains crawled slowly past the window, and Franz could see Mount Isel, with its memorial to Andreas Hofer, who had fought and died for the freedom of the Tyrol. As the train worked its way up through the alpine highlands to Mittenwald, Franz Reinisch saw his homeland disappear forever.

When the parents got home they found, lying inside the front door, a final letter from Franz:

Dearest parents

Once more may I say farewell to you. May I say from my heart a sincere 'may God reward you', that I was baptised and raised Catholic, to be brought up in life and suffering and in the glorifying of God; that I finally was able to receive the grace of priesthood as a pure unmerited gift from the hands of the one true high priest through the intercession of the dear Mother of God, so that during 14 years I could offer the Holy Mass and dispense many sacraments for the healing of souls.

Thanks to the holy Trinity, to the dear Mother of God, to the angels and saints, thanks to all the spiritual and material benefactors, whether still living or already dead.

Finally will I say thanks for the great grace to have been called to the Pallottines, above all to be able to work with Schönstatt, for the spreading of the Marian kingdom of Christ in the whole world.

So join with me in a happy and holy *Magnificat* and *Te Deum*, when you hear that my mission in this world is ended, and that it now begins in eternity.

May pain and joy join together in the great sea of love of the Father, Son and Holy Spirit.

My blessing also for my beloved brother and sisters and their children, and for my Tyrol homeland.

Be once more blessed by your thankful –

~ *Franz*

They carried it into the kitchen, and Papa Reinisch read it out to his wife. He laid it down, turned to his wife, who was weeping, and took her hand in his. 'Do you know what I've just thought of?' he said. 'Remember when the child Jesus went missing, and his parents were so upset over it? Remember his words when they found him? *Did you not know that I must be about my father's business?'*

BAMBERG, Bavaria, Germany. Tuesday, 14 April, 1942. This was the day for the call-up to military service for Franz Reinisch. Instead of reporting to Bad Kissingen, however, Franz called on a group of Schönstatt friends and stayed the night there. 'Coming late will be a small act of protest,' he told his friends.

That evening he wrote a letter to his provincial in the Pallottine Congregation, in which he made a request that was not to be divulged to anyone.

29

The ultimate test of man's conscience may be his willingness
to sacrifice something today for future generations
whose words of thanks will not be heard
Gaylord Nelson

BAD KISSINGEN, Bavaria, Germany. Wednesday, 15 April, 1942. Adolf Hitler gazes sternly across the entrance hall of Manteuffel Barracks, from out of a two-metre-high framed picture. The hall smells of sweat, boot leather and carbolic. At the desk below Hitler, a grey-haired, grey-faced sergeant is reading a newspaper, one foot up on a chair. A tall man in a long black overcoat stands facing him.

'My call-up papers,' the man says. The sergeant holds out his hand without looking up, and takes the proffered envelope. He opens it, takes out the folded sheet and glances through it. Something there makes him look up.

'You a padre, then?'

'I am.'

Only then does the sergeant notice the white clerical collar. He grunts and glances further down the page. He taps it as he looks up again: 'According to this, you should have been here yesterday. Twenty-four hours late reporting for duty. I have to say, padre, you don't seem to place too much value on becoming a soldier.'

'I'd place a lot more value on it,' the tall man says, 'if it were a different regime I'd be serving.'

A chill wind seems to have entered the bleak, boot-battered hall. The sergeant himself shivers: 'I – don't – think – I – heard – that,' he says.

'It's a lot worse than that, Sergeant,' the man says. 'I've come here to refuse military service. I'm not going to take the oath.'

'You're *WHAT?*'

'Let me say it again, sergeant. And listen carefully this time. *I am refusing military service.* I will not be taking the *Fahneneid.*'

BAD KISSINGEN, Monday, 20 April, 1942. The grey-haired sergeant looks up. Christ, not another bloody padre.

'My name is Josef Nägele,' the priest says. 'I've an appointment with the court officer. And I'm hoping to see Father Reinisch.'

'You mean *Private* Reinisch, I presume. Well good luck to you, Padre. We can get nowhere with him. He thinks he's another bloody Andreas Hofer and he wants to be a national hero. Well, that's not going to happen. It's not how they do things nowadays – there's other ways than shooting. They can soften up a prisoner with hard work and hunger.' The sergeant sighs. Then, more gently: 'But then, maybe he *will* succeed. He's a tough one, that.'

'Come in and sit down, Padre,' Major Arendt says. 'Am I glad to see you. You're from Schönstatt I take it?'

'Our Provincial asked me to come.' Father Nägele sits across from the green baize desk. 'He wants me to talk to Franz – to Father Reinisch.'

'Well, Padre, I hope you can talk some sense into him. I can get nowhere. It's like talking to a brick wall.'

'Think I don't know! I've known our Franzl a long time, Major. A brick wall it is.'

'You know, I didn't even arrest him that first evening,' Major Arendt says. 'I explained to him, let's first sleep on it, and we'll talk again in the morning. Then I sent for him the next morning – I didn't treat him as a recruit, but took the trouble to talk to him man to man. I even reminded him that we here are the *Sanitätskorps* [43], so that he'll only ever be carrying stretchers – most likely never a gun.

'But it soon became clear to me that he'd thought through his decision from every side; for he knew how to answer clear and sharp every objection.'

'That'd be our Franzl, to be sure.'

'You know, I still didn't have him arrested, as I kept hoping he'd change his mind. But when he began to express his attitude in front of the others I simply had no option. I had to put him under arrest. Would you like to see him now?'

'That's what I was hoping.'

---

[43] Medical Corps

The major twirls a handle on the desk. 'You can bring him now Sergeant,' he says. Then, turning to Nägele: 'Today's the Führer's birthday.' He smiled. 'Think that'll bring us luck?'

The door opens, a soldier leads in Franz Reinisch and goes back out. Franz is unshaven, dressed in ill-fitting old military fatigues and seems thinner. His face shows the stress of the last few days, days without even a smoke. The two men embrace as far as the handcuffs allow.

'I'm going to leave you men to it.' The major rises and goes to the door. 'I'll be up at the Colonel's office.'

There is a moment's silence after the door closes.

'There's no point in this, Josef,' Franz breaks the silence. His voice trembles. 'Make it short. Please.'

'Just listen for one moment, will you, Franz? Look, as a priest like yourself, I know as well as you that it would be out of the question for you to be unfaithful to your conscience.'

'And you'd be right. It *is* out of the question.'

' Just hear me out, please, Franz! Look, if I could believe that this was a mystery of grace, I would not try to change you. But it's not that. Your conduct simply does not comply with the objective norms of catholic morality, and must certainly from here on be seen as immoral. Do you hear what I'm saying? *Your conduct is immoral*, Franz. I don't know how your conscience can deal with that.'

'Have you finished, Josef?'

'Unfortunately, not quite.' Nägele sighed, stood up and drew a paper from his briefcase. 'I hate to do this, Franz, but I have a letter from Father Frank, our provincial, which I must now read to you. It's not very pleasant. I'll read you the relevant bit:

To Reverend Franz Dionysius Reinisch

Member, Pallottine Order

South German Province

Dear Father Reinisch

...In the moment in which you actually follow through your plan, you are, by virtue of my duty and power, based on Statute 210, without more ado you are dismissed from the Pallottine Order, and are stripped of the habit of the Order. Under your 'plan' I understand the refusal of the duty of Military Service or the Oath, so that you have to incur the severest penalty.

In the hope that you, in consideration of the word of the Lord, *Render unto Caesar the things that are Caesar's, and to God the things that are God's,* that you will rectify your conscience and abstain from your plan,

I am

Your well-meaning superior

Gez. *Josef Frank*

PS. Statute 210 prescribes the immediate expulsion from the Order, as well as the *remissio ad saeculum* [reduction to the lay state] if a great scandal is present, or if the behaviour of a brother threatens immediate grave injury.

The three men stand in front of the Colonel's desk – the major, and the two priests.

'Please sit down, gentlemen,' Colonel Ingerman says. 'Now Father' – he turns to Nägele – 'will you tell this soldier here why it's his duty to serve. We're treating him very gently, you know – I could have had him shot by now.'

'And I thank you for that, Colonel,' Franz speaks up. 'And I appreciate all your consideration here. I didn't expect it and I really do appreciate it.' He hesitates and seems close to tears. *'But I stand by my decision. I must.'*

The colonel rises, sighs. 'Then we've no way out, gentlemen. I'm afraid it's the Military Court in Würzburg. Nothing more we can do here.'

30

It is often said that second thoughts are best.
So they are in matters of judgment but
not in matters of conscience
John Henry Newman

WÜRZBURG, Germany. Thursday 23 April, 1942. At 9 a.m. in the military court building in Sedanstrasse, there comes a knock on the door of the Judge Advocate, Heinz Toyka.

'Enter.'

A young sergeant in the uniform of the Medical Reserve comes in, salutes. 'From Bad Kissingen, Herr *Kreigsgerichtsrat*. A book of evidence in regard of the soldier Franz Reinisch. The soldier is waiting in the corridor.'

'Under guard?'

'No Sir. There's only me.'

'How could you leave him like that?'

The young fellow's jaw drops. 'Er, Sir. He told me he wouldn't run away. He's – he's a priest. The other two guards are down in the canteen.'

'Good God. Go back out to him. I'll call you when I've read this.'

The sergeant salutes, clicks his heels and leaves.

A tall slim man in grey uniform steps into the room. It's his height that makes the first impression on Judge Advocate Toyka.

'Please sit, Father. I'll call you Father rather than Private, if that's OK.'

'Fine with me, Herr *Gerichtsrat.*' The voice is soft, Austrian accented.

Toyka asks the two women secretaries to leave the room. 'We need to be alone for the moment,' he says. He comes from behind his desk and sits across from Franz: 'Look, ah, I've just read this report. All about your coming late to call-up, and refusing the oath. It seems here they were pretty understanding in Bad Kissingen, but they couldn't move you. You stuck to your guns' – a smile – 'well not exactly guns. Am I right?'

'That's about it, yes.'

'So tell me about yourself. You're from Innsbruck, I gather? That anything to do with refusing the oath? I know you're with a German congregation, but – Hitler taking Austria and all that?'

'It's not nationalism, no. I guarantee that. But it's what Hitler *did* in Austria, and in the Rhineland too – everywhere, actually. Did? – *is still doing.* Rounding up Jews and shipping them off to God knows where. Beating them to death in the street. Ruling through terror. That *Nacht und Nebel* thing –

214

whisking people away so that they're never heard of again, so that no one even knows if they're alive or dead. Trying to destroy the churches and making himself the god of some mad Führer cult. Herr Gerichtsrat, there's no way I could serve such an evil regime – my conscience simply forbids it.'

'And I respect that, Father. I really do. I know the legitimate objections that Christians have against Nazi methods of power, and' – Toyka puts a finger to his lips – 'I agree with those objections. Well, with many of them, anyhow.

'But here's the thing you must remember: your Church – my Church, indeed (I'm a Catholic myself) – has not spoken against military service. And more than that, the attitude of your superiors flatly contradicts yours. Their wish and orders are for you to serve. Can you go against that?'

'That's what bothers me the most –'

'You've got to keep in mind the interests of the Church itself, of your order, indeed of your family. They'll all be terribly damaged by your refusing the oath. And by your execution, which will certainly follow.'

'I'm aware that I am going to be shot for this –'

'I hate to have to tell you, Father, that you're not going to be shot.'

'I'm not –?'

'Shooting is for soldiers. *You're going to be beheaded.* You see, you'll be a criminal, not a soldier. I'm afraid it's the *Fallbeil* for you – the guillotine.'

Franz stares at him. Then, with a hand to his mouth, he lurches towards the open window and vomits. And vomits until there is nothing left to vomit. Toyka stands by him with a gentle hand on his shoulder.

A tap on the door, and a secretary puts her head around it. Everything all right, Herr Gerichtsrat?' Her eyes widen at the scene by the window.

'Just leave us, Trudl, please. We'll be fine.'

Franz is shaking uncontrollably as they come away from the window. Sweat pours from his forehead. He sits back in the chair with his face in trembling hands. Toyka reaches into his desk and hands him a handkerchief. There is silence for minutes.

'Now do you see what we're up against?' Toyka almost whispers it.

'I never dreamt – I just never...' Franz can hardy speak.

'So. It looks a bit different now. eh?'

'Ja.' Franz can hardly utter it.

'You'll sign, then?'

The silence seems to last for ages. Toyka waits.

Franz breaks the silence: 'I cannot.'

'Good God, man –'

'Herr Gerichtsrat, I beg you to hear me. You are right – things do look different. So horribly different I can hardly bear to think. It's all changed – *but my conscience has not.* I'd change it if I could. But I cannot. *I cannot.* It's there and it simply won't go away.'

'Young man –'

'Please, I beg you listen, Herr Gerichtsrat. I know you're right about the Church's position, and I know my superiors want me to sign the oath. But none of it fits with my own

216

personal religious conscience, and in the end that's all I've got. I've struggled over this for years now. I knew it must come to this in the end – well, not the beheading. But I've long lived with my decision. I've said farewell to all my family in the Tyrol, There's no going back. I cannot go against my conscience.' He stops, astonished to see tears in the other man's eyes. 'Are you all right, Herr Gerichtsrat?'

Toyka's voice shakes. 'Have you any conception of what you are forcing on me? Look, I didn't ask to be your Judge Advocate. I didn't ask to decree your arrest. I don't want to decide your fate. You're forcing it on me.'

'Herr Gerichtsrat, I had no idea this would affect you so much.'

'Look, Father. I come from a good Catholic farming family – indeed I myself wanted to be a priest. It didn't happen. But now you're forcing me to proceed against a priest of God, which in my Mother's eyes would be a grave sin. For God's sake don't make me do this. I beg you, Father.' He stops, and now he too is weeping.

Franz gets up, goes across and puts a comforting arm around the man's shoulder. They are both in tears now.

Secretary Trudl puts her head around the door. Her jaw drops at the sight of the two weeping men and she quickly withdraws.

Franz is alone in the room when the door opens and Toyka returns. He stands in respect.

'Please sit, Father.' Toyka sits at his desk. He sighs: 'Well, I've been to see Dr Stoll. Nothing gained. As I told you, he's the

Oberkreigsgerichtsrat – the most senior judge here. And a Protestant, by the way. I outlined the case to him, and asked to be relieved of the further handling of it. He was very sympathetic and understanding, but he said no. He said I must see it through to the end.'

'I am so sorry, Herr Gerichtsrat. I truly am.'

'It's not your fault, Father. But now there's nothing else for me to do but open the warrant for your arrest –'

'But I'm already –'

'Those were formalities. This is different. This is the arrest that brings you before the War Court. My job now is to prepare the evidence for the court – it's all right here.' He opens the dossier. 'And to get you to sign here.' He pushes the file across the desk, and Franz moves over to sign it.

Toyka opens the door for the guard to come in and take the prisoner back to Bad Kissingen. The two men shake hands. 'May God go with you, Father,' Toyka says.

31

*The authority of the Church was thrown over by
the authority of the state. Twenty years only
have passed, and the authority of the state
is already thrown over by the
authority of conscience*
Lucy Beckett

BAD KISSINGEN, Bavaria, Germany. 7 May, 1942. 'I'm afraid
it's farewell, Private Reinisch,' the Colonel says. 'The order's
come to send you to Berlin. We're going to miss you – our
Catholic men here appreciated those Masses. And, perhaps I
shouldn't say it, Father, but your presence here has made a
difference. *Father* – I suppose I can still call you that.'

Franz stood before Colonel Ingerman's desk. He was finally
in a uniform that fitted, and he looked quite a splendid
specimen of a soldier of the Wehrmacht. His *Litzen* (collar
patches) were the dark blue of the Medical Corps.

'Now, Father, I've a request to make. We're badly short
staffed here, really badly – half of my men were taken last week
for the eastern front. I'm supposed to send you under guard,

but I literally can only spare one Feldwebel to go with you. He's just a young fellow. Could I trust you to make the journey, just with him? Would you give me your word – your parole?'

'I'm afraid I can't give it as a soldier, Herr Kommandant. How if I give it as a priest?'

'That will do fine, Father. And have a safe journey. Why don't you stay the night at Bamberg? Tegel aren't expecting you till the 8th. And, uh, given the circumstances, I won't ask for a salute.'

BAMBERG, Bavaria, Germany. 7 May, 1942. The lingering aroma of incense touched Franz's nostrils as he entered the sanctuary of the cathedral of Bamberg. He wore white gothic Mass vestments. Walking ahead of him, hands joined, was young Willi Kaufmann. He wore his Feldwebel's uniform, but his bearing reflected the altar server he had once been. There was a sprinkling of people in the pews. Some of them were Franz's Schönstatt friends from Bamberg.

As the little procession passed below the massive statue of the Bamberg Horseman, Franz looked up and thought with a momentary shudder how the Nazis had corrupted even that great equestrian figure, claiming that it signified Greater Germany looking to the East for new lands to conquer. He turned away and mounted the steps to the altar.

'*Introibo ad altare Dei...* I will go to the altar of God...'

'*Ad Deum qui laetificat juventutam meam...* To God who gives joy to my youth...'

As priest and server continued in the exchange of those sacred words, it was as if the past had returned for one brief glorious hour.

BERLIN: Tegel Military Prison, 9 May, 1942. A rattle of keys: the cell door swung open. The warder showed in an older man in military uniform, but without shoulder boards. A small cross hung from a chain around his neck. Franz noticed the tiny cross below the swastika on the man's cap just as he removed it.

'I'm acting chaplain here for the moment,' the visitor announced to Franz. 'Name is Voigt, Pastor Karl Voigt. Major Voigt, actually. I'm standing in for Chaplain Kreutzberg, and I've brought you Communion.'

'Oh, I thank God for that.' Franz knelt and grasped the priest's hand.

'Stand up, man. There's a few things need sorting out first. What's this nonsense about refusing the oath?'

'Oh, not that again, Father. I've been over this time and time again. For God's sake don't you start now. Why do you think I'm here in prison? If I'd signed I wouldn't be here at all.'

'Well, all I can say is, you ought to be ashamed of yourself. Utterly and thoroughly ashamed. I'm ashamed to have you as a fellow priest. Actually I can't even regard you as such. I regard you as a goddamn coward. Funking your duty to God and the Reich. You're a disgrace to your vocation. To – to your diocese, your order – whatever it is.'

'I'm a Pallottine, and also a member of Schönstatt.'

'So what have they to say to this nonsense?'

'They don't agree with me.'

'I should damn well think they don't. What they should do is expel you.'

'That's on the cards. But listen, Father. All you're doing is upsetting me. And I'm upset enough as it is. I'd rather you'd just leave me. But first – you did bring me Communion?'

'And I have no intention of letting you have it. You can do without Communion until you can see your way to do God's will. Right now you're unworthy of it. You'll get Communion when you come to your senses. When you quit this state of sin.'

'Very well, Father. And thank you for coming. Would you go now please? Please. *Just – GO!*'

After the cell door clanged shut, Franz collapsed shaking on his bunk and curled up with tears running through the fingers pressed to his face. 'Oh Jesus, no. No. O Jesus, mercy. O Mary my Mother help me. MTA, help me. *Help me. Help me...*'

BERLIN, 15 May, 1942. Office of the Military Bishop of the Wehrmacht. Bishop Franz Josef Rarkowski was delighted to see Father Kreutzberg back. 'You've been badly missed, Heinrich,' he said, leading the priest into his study. 'You'll be starting in Tegel next week. At least they'll have a proper chaplain then.

'That Voigt fellow's causing me a lot of problems. He fights with everyone, and he told those poor fellows up in Section Four they deserve their death sentences. Talk about God's mercy – I doubt if he ever heard of it. Well, he'll be heading east soon – he'll be needing God's mercy there.

222

'Which reminds me. I've a letter here from the Pallottines – the head of the South German Province. He says a few days ago a Father Reinisch came to Tegel for refusing the oath. Apparently he says it's on account of the anti-christian character of the regime – his words, by the way. Not mine! Anyhow, he's one of their men – a Pallottine.

'We must take an interest in this priest. See if you can find him and if you can do something for him.'

32

The antagonism between life and conscience
may be removed either by a change of life
or by a change of conscience
Leo Tolstoy

BERLIN: Tegel Military Prison, 25 June, 1942. The stone walls seemed to vibrate grief as they echoed the clang of boots on metal, from the soldier accompanying Father Heinrich Kreutzberg up the iron stairs to the intersection on the prison's first floor. As always the prison odour assailed his nostrils – that miasma in which fumigant failed in its fight against filth, sweat, excrement, urine, vomit and semen. The stench of despair.

From the intersection one had an overview of floors extending in the form of a cross for about 60 metres. A *Feldwebel* sat at a desk in the intersection.

'I'm looking for the *sanitäts* soldier Franz Reinisch, Herr Feldwebel,' Kreutzberg said to him.

The feldwebel consulted his file. 'Section 4, cell 53. That's up on the second floor, right over the entrance wing. Last cell but two. He's alone in the cell.' He gave a low whistle. 'That's where the death candidates are, Padre. It's a bit dismal up there.'

The cell door clunked behind him as Pastor Kreutzberg saw Franz Reinisch for the first time. He noted the upright stance, the resolute mouth, perhaps suggesting courage and decision. He quickly took in the surroundings – the high barred window; tin bucket in one corner; a small table and stool at the far right; two small books on the table, both black with gilt edges; a folding trestle bunk on the left, almost touching both walls – how could this tall fellow fit into that?

Franz announced himself: 'Franz Reinisch, priest, Pallottine Order, under examination because of the refusal to take the military oath.' He bowed slightly.

'Heinrich Kreutzberg, your new Catholic chaplain here.' He held out his hand. 'Now, Reinisch, tell me briefly why you want to refuse the oath. No. We can get to that later. First tell me a bit about yourself. Where you're from, a bit of your history, where you've worked. That sort of thing. Let's sit down – I'll take the bunk here. You take the chair.'

Franz took him briefly through his life's story. When he came to his joining Schönstatt, Kreutzberg clapped his hands: 'Confrère Reinisch, I don't believe it! Heavens, I'm in the Movement too. Amazing we've not met – but of course I never worked at Vallendar. Well, that really makes us brothers, doesn't it? Our trust in God's Mother. The MTA will see us through. She always does.'

He stood up to take a small packet from his overcoat pocket. 'Now I have a great joy for you – I've brought you the Blessed

Sacrament. I'm leaving some Sacred Hosts permanently here with you, so you may take Communion every morning.'

Tears seemed to come easily to Franz during these days of anguish, but for once these were tears of joy. On bended knees he silently took the packet, kissed it, wrapped it in a handkerchief, rose and put it at the far end of the table against the wall beside the black volumes. He came across to Kreutzberg and embraced him.

'I heard what happened with Chaplain Voigt,' Kreutzberg said.

'He meant no harm, I'm sure. I suppose it was his way of trying to change my mind.'

Kreutzberg pulled out a packet of cigarettes, took one and offered one to Franz.

'I don't smoke Father. Off them since my arrest. It was hell – never thought I could manage it. Well, *I* didn't. I think it was the MTA!'

'Which brings us to – well, you know what. Dear Brother, you want to refuse the oath, and I will not try to change your mind. That I promise. But I do have a request for you. Would you write out for me fully the reasons why you have reached this decision – why you are refusing the oath? You see, it's also for me a huge responsibility, as your chaplain, to guide you appropriately. And so I must have full clarity about your purpose.'

'I'd be only too happy to do that, Father. I'll start this very afternoon. God knows I have the time here.'

'I brought you some paper, and pencils. I'm afraid they wouldn't let me take in ink. And now, dear Brother, I have one more request. Would you write out for me during these days all your experiences, aspirations and feelings. Your thoughts about the past and present experiences, and even your thoughts about the future?'

For the first time Kreutzberg experienced that flash of sudden anger that Franz was capable of. 'I certainly will not, Father. I'll do nothing of the sort. My feelings are my own, and I'll have nobody probing around among them. They're my bloody business. Don't you ask me that again.'

'Easy, Father. Take it easy. Sorry I asked.'

The two sat in silence.

After a while Kreutzberg spoke up. 'Can I tell you something, Brother? Now – I'm not asking anything. But – I'd just like you to think about something. You're standing by your conscience, that much I know. Now, whether you're right or wrong, conscience is the ultimate arbiter. We've nothing else. As Aquinas says. Now, whatever happens to you, a person holding to his conscience can have a profound effect on people. Especially if – especially if one pays the ultimate price for it.

'But if no one knows the thoughts and feelings that led to it, all of it is wasted. No, not the stand or the deed – they're never wasted. But the example. People live by example – all the sermons in the world don't add up to one example. But if it's not known...? Think what your written word could achieve later, when circumstances permit. Will you think about that, Brother?'

The flash of anger was gone. 'I'll think about it, Father. But – don't push me anymore right now. All right?'

'That's fine, dear Brother.' Kreutzberg glanced at his watch. 'And now it's near lock-up time – I'd better be going. By the way, could I bring you a few books – ?'

'I have my *New Testament.*' Franz pointed to one of the books on the table. 'That's my comfort book. It's all I need. Well, that and my breviary.'[44] He knelt. 'And now, Father, will you bless me before you go?'

In the days and weeks that followed, Kreutzberg was Franz's link with the world, and indeed with the spiritual world. He regularly brought him enough Sacred Hosts to take him through the days until his next visit. The visits were often far apart, as Kreutzberg had to look after souls in two of Berlin's prisons – Spandau as well as Tegel.

He had to prepare men for death, and to attend at regular executions. These took place by firing squad at Tegel and Spandau, as the Wehrmacht were only competent for firing squads. The beheadings, reserved for criminals, took place under the auspices of the civil authorities at Brandenburg.

Franz finally agreed to keep a diary of his thoughts and feelings and kept it up until near the end.

---

[44] The *breviary* is the book of a priest's daily prayer – known as the *Divine Office.*

33

A life laid down cannot be reclaimed,
nor can a ruined conscience
Aleksandr Solzhenitsyn

BERLIN: Tegel Military Prison, 2 July, 1942. Franz Reinisch was unusually quiet when Pastor Kreutzberg came to visit. Without a word he handed him a long, legal-looking manila envelope, sealed with red wax and a swastika. The seal had been broken and Kreutzberg pulled out the document.

'The court summons,' Franz said. 'It's for Thursday.'

The document was clear enough:

ARREST MATTER
PROSECUTION ORDER

Against the soldier Franz Dionysius Reinisch,...in Bad Kissingen, born 1.2.1903 in Feldkirch, catholic, citizen of the Reich, single, no criminal record, in civil life a priest, in custody since 15.4.1942, in military examination custody, Tegel branch, the following charge is ordered:

The accused is suspected, since 15.4.1942 in Bad Kissingen, Würtsburg and Berlin, of having attempted to completely avoid military service – a crime against Paragraph 5 Abs. 1 Nr. 3 KSSVO.

The accused was born on 1.2.1903 as the son of finance officer Franz Reinisch and his wife Maria née Huber...

The document went on to give a fairly comprehensive summary of Franz's life, up to the time of his call up for military service:

On 6.4.1942 he received an enlistment order, to present himself on 14.4.1942 at the Reserve Medical Corps 13 in Bad Kissingen. He presented himself only on 15.4.1942 and was attached to the 3rd Company. When the sergeant, on account of his late reporting for duty, put him the question, whether he set much store on being a soldier, he answered, 'I would set store by it if the present regime were not at the helm.' Thereupon – after he was put in uniform – he was arrested.

During his interrogation by the military court officer, he declared that he, through his late reporting to the troop, had wanted from the outset to express that he knew neither fear nor flight, but that however he did not agree with the call-up order... He respected and honoured the German Army, but regretted that it was misused by the Nazi Party. He loved the German people, especially his Tyrol homeland; for that reason he saw himself forced to fight against National Socialism in his homeland, even to the giving up of his life.

At his magistrate's hearing through the Court of the 173 Division in Würzburg the accused had stuck by his standpoint and renewed his determined will to refuse the oath. Referring to the consequences of his decision, he made clear that he for a year and a half had wrestled with his decision, and that he now was clear and ready to go to his death for his conviction. He did not consider any change of his conviction... Yet he could not be accused of being an enemy of the state, in that he refused military service to the present regime. For any other regime he would take the oath in defense of the Fatherland.

Again at the examination by the interrogator of the Reich Military Court the accused had steadfastly held to his standpoint and explained that his conviction, that he carefully reached, required that he would refuse the oath and thus his military service, and that he, even if he considered the consequence, would not be wavering in his resolve.

The accused had taken the same standpoint again in a letter to the Provincial of the Pallottines.

The conduct of the accused is a continued offence of decay of the fighting spirit, in the sense of Paragraph 5 Abs.1 Nr. 3 KSSVO. The accused, who is a Reich German of military age, is become a soldier through the call-up to military service, and as such obliged to active military service. He also is aware of this. That his refusal of military service stems from religious or political conviction respectively, has no bearing on his punishable guilt.

A deciding factor in this, that the accountability of the accused was in some way impaired, does not apply, according to the expert opinion of the senior military medic, Dr Schmidt.

Evidence

The admission of the accused, pages 1, 3, 7, 15

The expertise of Dr Schmidt in Berlin

The extract from the military roll call

The extract from the register of felonies, included with the document cover

The letter of the accused, page (sheet 21 a).

Signed,

On behalf of the President of the Reich War Court

BASTIAN, Admiral

Representing the Reich War Court

SCHRAG, Senior Judge Advocate

Kreutzberg replaced the document in its manila cover and handed it back to Franz. 'You know what this means?' he said.

'It's my death, come one step closer,' came the answer. Franz thought for a moment. 'You know I keep thinking of those words from St John's Gospel, *If the corn does not fall into the earth and die, it remains alone; but if it dies, it brings much fruit.*'

BERLIN-Charlottenburg. 7 July, 1942. A closed prison van took Franz Reinisch to the Reich Military Court in Witzlebenstraße. There was a long wait in an outer room before the proceedings began at 11.15 a.m.

Although it was nominally a public hearing, there were only a few people in the room – a prosecutor, a defender, a registrar, and one soldier on guard who stood against the wall. All wore the grey uniforms of the Wehrmacht. There was a raised dais, and a row of benches on the floor of the room. Franz sat at the end of the front bench.

Everyone stood when the Court President swept into the room and up onto the dais. A bald man in his sixties with a thick neck pushing against his military collar, he was clearly in a foul mood. 'Heil Hitler!' he snapped, stretching his arm in the salute.

'Heil Hitler!' All arms rose, except that of Franz Reinisch.

This did not help the President's mood. He launched straight into the matter of Franz coming late to the barracks.

'Utterly childish behaviour, Reinisch. I've never heard the like.' He slapped the dossier in front of him. 'Sulking like a ten-year-old. Why don't you tell the court why you're sulking? Well, *I'll* tell them. It's because the Gestapo banned you from preaching, and closed a couple of subversive seminaries, that's why. And absolutely right they were. Stopping your subversive nonsense. Well, we'll be putting a permanent stop to all your *Scheissdreck.* [45] What have you to say to that?'

Franz stood. 'Honourable court. I respect and treasure the German Army, because truly religious and morally upright people belong to it, and because the German army has protected the homeland from enemy attack, and because I still expect right and justice from it more than anywhere else. And

---

[45] Shit

235

so, as Paul before King Agrippa, I ask you, Herr Senatspräsident, to hear me with patience.

'In regard to my late arrival at the barracks in Bad Kissingen, this did not come from sulking, as the honourable Senatspräsident suggests, but strictly from principle. This principle – that I do not recognise the present regime, *and therefore it has no orders to give me.*

'Nor is it childish, Herr Senatspräsident, that I am concerned for those seminaries which the Gestapo has shut down, because I am concerned for the priesthood which they are trying to destroy –'

'Don't give us any of that political propaganda trash!' the President interrupted, slamming down his gavel. 'This is no goddam church court, but a military court. And you'd better remember that. We have no respect for you at all here, when you know that today it's all about Bolshevism. You present yourself here, if I may make a comparison, as if in a burning house, to rescue your belongings, and let the others perish. You can happily have your two seminaries and let the whole German people go under. And it doesn't seem to matter that ten thousand of your colleagues have taken the oath.'

Franz's temper flared: 'Herr Senatspräsident. Earlier you used a word which I now feel free to use too. You've just mentioned how many of my priest colleagues have taken the oath. Well I should like to recall a saying we had as children in the Tyrol: *Friss mal Scheissdreck* – "Eat shit – a million flies can't be wrong".'

The court erupted in laughter, with the President furiously slamming his gavel.

236

'How dare you!' he roared at Franz. 'How dare you disrespect the court like this! You'll pay for this, and a lot sooner than you think!'

'May I continue, Herr Senatspräsident?' Franz was trembling with anger. 'You've spoken of Catholic priests and how they are serving the regime. I fear that is what is to be regretted about this present regime – its two-facedness. On the one hand it makes the Catholic priesthood impossible through the Gestapo; on the other hand the priest is expected to hold his own and give his all to the regime.'

The two angry men glared at each other.

'Listen here, Reinisch.' The President spluttered. 'This court has no respect for you. *I* have no respect for you. Your arguments are *Scheissdreck*. I despise you and your goddam priestcraft. I've had other soldiers here before me – Carinthians and Tyroleans even – and I respect them and value them far more than I could ever respect you. Look, I'm asking you one more time. *Will – you – or – will – you – not – take – the – oath?*'

'I must make a distinction –'

'No distinctions. I want a clear yes or no. Same as the Bible: *The lukewarm will be vomited out. He who is not with me is against me.* The oath, Reinisch. Will you take the oath?

'My conscience says NO.'

'Conscience? You and your miserable little conscience. You set your tiny conscience against the massive need of the Greater German People. Do you know what the Führer said about conscience? He said it was like circumcision – an invention of the Jews to weaken human nature. It's certainly done that to you. Don't talk to me about conscience. One last time: will you stow that damn conscience and take the oath?'

'*NEIN.*'

The prosecutor rose and spoke for the first time. There was no need to outline a case against the accused. Franz had done it for him. 'Herr Senatspräsident, I hereby propose that the penalty of death be pronounced by this court. And that the penalty be beheading, as befits a criminal rather than a soldier.'

'Defending counsel?'

'Nothing really to say, Herr Senatspräsident, except to suggest that perhaps, in the loneliness of his cell, the accused might still reflect on his decision.'

'Reinisch. You have the final word.'

The prisoner rose for the final time, his anger simmering down. 'Herr Senatspräsident, I ask you to have patience here. I will make no political propaganda, but I will only make clear my standpoint –'

'We don't want any more of your standpoint, soldier. We've heard it enough times. This court accuses you of pride. You are a satanically proud man, and you'll pay for that pride just as Satan did. And don't forget that all you clergy are paid by the state. What would the Pope make of his Catholic Church, if the church no longer got its salaries from the state? You could pack up, that's what. And now, Reinisch, have you anything else to say?'

'On the basis of this procedure I declare, one more time: No, *I WILL NOT SERVE!*'

Franz remained in the court, alone with the armed guard, while the decision of life or death was being made in the adjoining room. Not that there would be much deciding, he knew. He closed his eyes and prayed: 'MTA, take me as a sacrifice, if it pleases you.'

The door opened and the court personnel came back into the room. All seemed to avoid Franz's eye.

The registrar rose. 'The *Sanitäts* soldier Franz Dionysius Reinisch is, because of his refusal of the Military Oath and his undermining of the military, condemned to death, the execution to be effected by beheading under the *Fallbeil*. The *Senatspräsident* demands the sentence on the grounds that the accused, in this heavy hour in the fight against Bolshevism, has deserted the Fatherland.'

34

If a superior gives any order to one who is under him
which is against that man's conscience
although he do not obey it, yet
he shall not be dismissed
St Francis of Assisi

BERLIN: Tegel Military Prison, 10 July, 1942. 11 a.m. Pastor Kreutzberg was astonished at the peace that seems to radiate from Franz Reinisch. The hideous fate, so lately pronounced, seemed to be completely accepted.

'I'm offering it as a sacrifice to the MTA,' he told the pastor. 'For Austria and for Germany, that they will soon be free of all this.'

'Ah, I have a difficult task for you, Franz.' Kreutzberg hesitated. 'Your superiors have asked me to do them a favour. They've drawn up a list of questions for you, about refusing the oath, and they would like you to answer them. Could I read you some of them?'

'Why not?'

'And you just answer what comes into your mind. We can write them out more carefully later. All right?'

'Go right ahead.'

'Fine. Here goes then. First question. The Superior asks: The way up to now is God's providence, including a readiness to die. Is not taking the oath a part of that readiness, and a way of God?'

'I simply have no reason to change my mind.'

'Fine. Next question. The oath is not demanded without authority. Hitler is the representative of God-given authority, in as much as he is head of state. So the oath requires our obedience.'

'Not mine. An oath can only require obedience if it can be totally sworn to. Totally. So I cannot take the oath with reservations. And given what Hitler is doing to Christianity, and to our Jewish people, I would have to make reservations in an oath of loyalty to him. And that I cannot do.'

'If your superiors order you under obedience?'

'They can't oblige me to something against my conscience.'

Kreutzberg smiled and threw up his hands. 'Just as I expected, Franz. No change. But that's not all, I'm afraid. I'm afraid your local superior is waiting downstairs. He wants to see you.'

'Father Keller? What's he here for?'

'He just wants a word with you. Will you see him?'

'Not if he's going to start again about the oath.'

'Please. Just let him talk to you. He says he has news for you.'

A warder handcuffed Franz before bringing him down to the visitor's room, and stood across from the table where the superior was waiting. Keller stood and leaned over to shake the manacled hands. Franz sat down opposite him.

The superior got nowhere. Every time he tried to bring the conversation around to the oath, Franz countered with: 'Tell me, how is Father Clissman? His health any better? And Brother Ignatius?'

Finally Keller came to the point. 'I am here to tell you, Father, that you have been ordered, under formal precept, to take this oath. Which means that, if you refuse, you will be guilty of formal disobedience to your lawful superiors. Which, as you know, is gravely sinful.'

Franz stared at him, anger rising. 'I find this hard to believe, Father. How could you – how could they – try this on me! You people – I thought you were my friends. My brethren. Well, here's my answer, and you can tell them from me. It's what we were all taught from Aquinas: *In discipline, always obedience; in spiritual things, always conscience.* Tell them that. They should bloody well know it anyhow.'

Keller moved uncomfortably. 'I have some more bad news for you, I'm afraid. The provincial council are considering your expulsion from the Pallottines. That is, if you continue to refuse the Oath.'

Franz stood up and, for a moment, his superior thought he was going to be hit. The guard moved in closer.

But in fact Franz was not as agitated as expected. 'This isn't exactly news, Father,' he said. 'You don't seem to be aware that they threatened that back in April. So just you tell them to go ahead if they want. Maybe it will keep the Gestapo off their backs.'

INNSBRUCK, Austria. 15 July, 1942. Remnants of snow still glinted on the Hafelekarspitze, visible through the north-facing window where Reinisch Senior sat with Father Keller. Below the window the River Inn flowed placidly.

Maria Reinisch brought in coffee and sat down with the two men. A gentle woman with strong grey hair, round rimmed spectacles, her quietness contrasted with the authority of her husband. His broad moustache, old-style collar, and watch chain across the waistcoat, gave the appearance of the senior civil servant that he was.

'The situation can still be saved, Herr Councillor,' Father Keller was saying. 'I have it on good authority that everything will go into reverse if your son takes the oath. The death sentence will be lifted. He will be released from prison so he can take his place in the Medical Corps. A totally clean slate. He could even have a chance to become a chaplain. Imagine what he could do for souls in the military.'

'Why are they being so lenient?' Papa Reinisch asked. 'They must surely be very angry with Franzl.'

'It's seems to be all about avoiding scandal,' Keller said. 'The authorities know that even if your son is executed, word will get out that someone somewhere refused the Oath and dared to question Nazi doctrine. Very few have, so far. And that could bring the whole house down. Well, it could certainly start people thinking and questioning. And they will do absolutely anything to avoid that. And to avoid creating martyrs.'

'So what can we do to help?' Maria looked at her husband.

'Well, Ma'am. A word from you and your husband here might just work the miracle. You are probably the only people in the world your son would listen to now. A letter from you, Sir, or one from both of you...'

Papa Reinisch got up and went to the window. Hands behind his back, he stood looking out at the peaks high above the roofs.

'No,' he said. 'There'll be no letter from us. Certainly none to ask him to change. Our Franzl is old enough to make up his own mind. Only *he* knows what he has to do, and it's not our place to tell him.'

Maria went across to the window and put a gentle hand on her husband's arm.

'Besides,' Reinisch Senior added, 'I'm thinking along the same lines myself.'

35

My conscience is captive to the Word of God. I cannot and
I will not recant anything, since it is neither safe
nor right to go against conscience.
May God help me. Amen
Martin Luther

BERLIN-Charlottenburg. 25 July, 1942. 11 a.m. Franz
Reinisch waited quietly in the ante room of the military court.
His handcuffs had been removed and he had his small
prayerbook in his hand. Pastor Kreutzberg was with him. A
soldier stood on guard by the door.

Franz broke the silence. 'You know what day this is, Father?
The 25th of July – my Chancellor's anniversary. Remember?'

'It must be eight years now, wouldn't it be?'

'Poor old Dollfuss. He did his best for Austria: sure that's
why they killed him. And they're still at it, the bastards.
Murdering, I mean.

'Tell me, why do you think they have me back here again?
To soften me up, is it?' Franz grew quiet for a moment. 'You
know, today's the feast of the Apostle James. I was reading the

Epistle for the Mass, and it says, how God places us apostles on the last place *as those who are consecrated to death.*

'Apt, isn't it? Consecrated to death. Indeed the message is all through today's Mass, as though it was meant for me. In the Alleluia chorus it says here*: I've chosen you out of the world so that you can go there and bring fruit: and your fruit will remain.* And in the Gospel, Jesus says: *You know not what you ask. Can you drink from the chalice that I will drink? They said, we can. Then he said, My chalice shall you drink.'* Franz breathed deeply. 'Oh God. Oh God, give me the strength to go through with this. And bring the cup soon – if it must come. Don't have me wait too long.'

The door opened and Franz Reinisch was led into the courtroom. It was the same one as before, except this time there was no one there but a judge. The accompanying guard was sent from the room.

The judge was white haired and clearly in his 70s. He seemed friendly, even kind. He left the dais, came down to sit with Franz, and took him by the hand. 'Look,' he began, 'I'm old enough to be your father.'

Franz was taken aback, and quite moved. It was certainly pleasanter than the snarling, gavel-thumping bully of the previous occasion. He began to relax.

'I wanted to be alone with you,' the older man said, 'because there's a few things I couldn't really say out loud. And I'll tell you one of them – this Thousand-Year Reich is a load of rubbish. It won't last beyond Hitler's lifetime. But for God's sake don't ever repeat what I said. Can I trust you?'

'Well, I don't want any more people ending up like me. So yes, I think you can trust me.'

'Look, Son, we've both studied history, and it's full of men like Hitler. Genghis Kahn. Napoleon. Fellows like Robespierre. They never last. Here today and gone tomorrow. So I'd never dream of asking you to fight for a man like that.'

This was different. Something Franz had never expected to hear. He felt a little less alone.

'So we must all stand together, son. We're not really concerned about this Hitler fellow. This here is about the survival of the German People, not that of any regime. This is a war between Bolshevism and Christianity.'

That touched a nerve in Franz. 'What I find hard to take, Herr Gerichtsrat, is that here in the Homeland there's also a war against Christianity. The Nazis are trying to destroy us as much as Bolshevism is. I find it hard to see the difference.'

'The Nazis won't last too long after we've won against the Bolshevists. But we've got to settle with them first. And that's why this oath is important. We must all take up the fight.'

'Where does Providence come into all this, Herr Gerichtsrat?'

'Providence? Huh. I'm afraid I don't set much store by Providence. It left us in the shit in 1918. And what does Providence mean, anyhow?'

A brief anger: 'You sound like Pilate, asking *What is Truth?* It seems to me, Herr Gerichtsrat, that you have only a political concept of God. If God helps, then He exists. If not, then He doesn't exist.'

'You're a bit hard on me, Son. I'm a genuine Christian just like yourself. A Lutheran, actually.'

'But why do you all keep bringing me back? I don't know how many times I've been arrested – or arraigned, or whatever it is you're at.'

'It's this simple, my boy. The authorities want you to sign. They will do anything to achieve this, because they know the consequences for the regime if you don't: the word would leak all over the country. And give ideas to others. So I know for a fact that you will walk free immediately you sign – even at the very last moment. I've been told as much.

'But I'm not concerned with those consequences. I want something more – I want to save your life. You're just too good a man for Germany to lose. Come on, son. There's a pen. And there's where you sign. Would you do this for me – no, would you do it for Germany?'

Franz gave a great, heartfelt sigh. 'Oh, God, I wish I could, Herr Gerichtsrat. I truly wish to God I could.'

BERLIN: Tegel Military Prison, 25 July, 1942. 7 p.m. Franz Reinisch sat in his cell with Pastor Kreutzberg. 'Do you know what the guard said to me in the van, on our way back here? "This'll be the last time," he said. "Next time it'll be St Peter." What do you think he meant?'

'I think we both know what he meant,' Kreutzberg said.

'I suppose you're right. But you know something? I've never felt happier. There were two letters waiting for me when I got back, both from my parents. D'y'know what my Father said? "Stay strong, Franzl," he said. "An easy conscience is a soft resting cushion." And Mother said she'd pray and sacrifice even more, and that Heaven is our reward. Know something? I hope the Gestapo didn't read this –'

'You can be sure they did. But I wouldn't worry too much. If they haven't moved by now, they're hardly going to. They've bigger fish to fry these days.'

'I hope you're right. You know something, Heinrich. Do you know that in my first weeks here, I used to have a terrible temptation? I was in such despair that, when we were exercising in the prison yard, I felt a longing to throw myself on the guard, so I could just get a bullet and be free of it all. That went on for days. But prayer got me through in the end.

'Well today I haven't an iota of despair. What I have is a longing for heaven. When we came out from the court today, the sun was shining in a blue sky and there was a thrush singing its head off in a tree right above us. My heart just lifted. I feel now I've never been nearer to Heaven. And I can hardly wait to get there.'

After Kreutzberg had left, Franz lay on his bunk and let the euphoria sweep over him. His thoughts wandered to mountain pastures of the Tyrol, to the little onion-domed churches in the valleys, to those hikes through the Karwendel Alps and those summer trips to Feldkirch and the Vorarlberg. He found himself murmuring those lovely words:

> On my oath, Tiroler Land
> Hand and hearts are raised
> Therefore we pledge anew
> Heart of Jesus, ever true to thee

But his longing was not for the mountains of home, but for those strange and mysterious heights where his faith told him he would soon arrive. As he closed his eyelids to sleep, he was at peace.

Suddenly a loud and dreadful wailing broke out from somewhere down the corridor. It rose and fell, rising to a shriek, vibrating utter desolation and despair. Quickly it was picked up from other cells, until the whole prison block seemed to reverberate.

Tranquillity shattered, Franz listened. He longed to go to those cells and take someone's hand and utter words of hope or a blessing by which he might share his peace. But there was no way he could.

He knelt and prayed for those anguished souls, that God would send them comfort. He kept trying to imagine each one alone in his cell. *Turn your face to them, O Lord, and give them peace,* was his prayer. *And Mary, MTA, be a mother to them.* He whispered the words over and over.

Perhaps the prayer worked. Perhaps not. But gradually the wailing died, and at last the silence of the grave descended on the prison. By then the moon was up and the shadow of the window bars had formed the shape of a cross on the cell wall.

36

He who sacrifices his conscience to ambition
burns a picture to obtain the ashes
Chinese proverb

BERLIN: Tegel Military Prison. 27 July, 1942. 11.50 a.m. Franz Reinisch reached across to his table and lifted off a few sheets of paper. 'It looks as if they won't be bothering me to testify anymore,' he said to Pastor Kreutzberg. 'At least I hope not. But you know how they'll twist my words after I'm gone. So I've decided to take up your suggestion, and put my thoughts in writing. So when I'm gone there'll be at least something clear and definite.'

Kreutzberg accepted the sheaf of paper, put on his spectacles and glanced at the pencilled lines. Clear sharp handwriting.

Franz: 'I want you to make copies of this, Heinrich. I want at least one to go to the authorities. And I want one to go to the Pallottines. And at least one to Schönstatt. And if we could ever get one to Josef Kentenich in Dachau – but that's a non-runner. Well, he'd know the contents anyway without ever reading it. And of course a copy to my parents. By the way, would you be safe taking this out?'

'Don't I take your diary pages out? They never search me, and this will be inside my coat. It'll be fine. Do you mind if I have a quick glance through it now?'

'Go right ahead.'

The thinking was as clear and sharp as the handwriting:

SINCE today in the struggle against bolshevism, it is a matter of saving the Christian Faith and the German homeland, and, as the proceedings of the Herr President of the Senate himself made clear, also a matter of saving the Christian Occident, so the condemned man believes that he must unwaveringly hold to the reasoning he has held up to now.

For this time of war is primarily being used, here in our homeland, to rip out from the hearts of the people and especially of the youth (as lots of examples testify) belief in the God-Man Jesus Christ – as a result of which the soldiers at the front, through their leave and through letters from their relatives, are enormously shaken in their military zeal.

From Russia there came to me men on leave, hardly without exception fathers of families, and explained to me: 'What's the point of our fight? We're fighting against foreign bolshevism, but we seem to be fighting for bolshevism here at home – for example, the taking out of crucifixes from the schools, the suppression of cloisters, and closing of churches.'

The condemned is no revolutionary, i.e., an enemy of the state and people, who fights with fist and force; he is a Catholic priest who uses the weapons of spirit and faith. And he knows for what he fights.

It is obvious, therefore, that one must first make ineffective those powers that are bringing about this destruction of our strength to fight. However as the present government do not in the least put a stop to these powers but even favour them, so this prisoner believes that, by refusing the oath to the present government rather than to the German people, he is holding true in his life struggle, rather than the opposite.

He is therefore gladly ready, for Christ the King and for the German Homeland, to offer up his life, so that Christ the Lord may overcome these antichristian and bolshevist powers and might from abroad, but also here at home, so that our people will once more become a strong and free people of God amidst the people of the East.

Berlin-Tegel, 26 July 1942
gez. *Franz Reinisch*

Kreutzberg tilted up his spectacles. 'Couldn't be clearer,' he said. 'This is for posterity, I take it you realize that?'

Franz nodded.

'I'll see it's kept for them,' Kreutzberg assured him. 'It could be part of a book someday.'

'Never will I go back on this, Heinrich. Even after they silence me. You'll see to it, won't you?'

'That I promise, Franzl.'

BERLIN: Tegel Military Prison, 7 August, 1942. 1 p.m. When Pastor Kreutzberg came into Cell 53 he found Franz Reinisch, so usually tranquil, strangely uneasy.

'On Wednesday afternoon I got terribly agitated,' Franz told him. 'And I've been like that for the last couple of days. I don't know what it is – maybe it's that I've made an enemy of the Senatspräsident, or something like that. Or maybe – maybe they've confirmed my sentence.'

Kreutzberg sat down on the edge of the bunk. He hesitated. 'Which would you rather, Franz – if you have to go, would you rather have it sooner than later? If – if there's to be a final decision – would you like it as early or as late as possible?'

Franz thought for a moment. 'Better early, I think. This uncertainty make me fidgety. This in and out of courts, this back and forth, whether God and Mary will accept or not the offer of my life. It just goes on and on.' There was a pause. Then he turned and looked directly at his friend. 'Is there something you know? Something that *I* don't?'

This was the critical moment, and Kreutzberg could not dodge it. Instead of an answer, he closed his eyes affirmatively.

'Is the sentence confirmed?'

Kreutzberg nodded slightly.

'Oh, thanks be to God!' Franz cried out. There and then he knelt down and prayed.

Kreutzberg laid a hand on his shoulder and waited in silence. At length Franz made the sign of the cross and stood up. All agitation was gone. There seemed even joy and serenity in his face.

Kreutzberg reached up, placed his hands on the man's head, and uttered a blessing. It was the Feast of the Sacred Heart.

BERLIN: Tegel Military Prison, 8 August, 1942. 10 a.m. When Kreutzberg came to visit, Franz Reinisch handed him the black-and-gold book he cherished – his precious New Testament. 'Will you see that my Mother gets this?' he asked.

Kreutzberg thumbed through a few of the gilt-edged pages. They were covered in red and blue underscoring, and the margins were crammed with notes. 'Would you not rather keep this – for the time being, at least?' he asked.

'Just take it please, Heinrich. And tell my mother how much joy I have in my heart right now. Since you brought me the confirmation of the sentence, I can put myself at rest about it. I can hardly believe I could ever feel like this: my mood is one long Te Deum and Magnificat. *My soul doth magnify the Lord...* It's extraordinary.

'Everything's OK now. I'll endure in faithfulness to the end. True to prayer; keeping order in my cell so that the service people will have nothing to complain about. I'm just – well, just *ready*.'

37

Through pride we are ever deceiving ourselves. But deep down below the surface of the average conscience a still, small voice says to us, something is out of tune

Carl Jung

BERLIN: Tegel Military Prison, 9 August, 1942. 10 a.m. After Pastor Kreutzberg arrived he spent the following three hours visiting his other charges throughout the prison. When he reached Cell 53 he was surprised to see the cell door open.

Franz sat inside, but instead of his usual army uniform he wore a grey-green drill suit. 'This is it,' he said. 'I've just changed. They'll be coming for me any minute now. No more soldier's uniform – I'm a criminal now!'

'But –'

'Don't worry, Heinrich. They're not going to execute me. Well, not right now! They're taking me off to Brandenburg. As you know, that's where they do the head chopping – they can only shoot me here. And of course that would be too good for me. Shooting's for soldiers, not for criminals. So it's farewell, my friend, I fear.'

Kreutzberg could find no words.

Reinisch went to the little table, lifted off his breviary and a couple of Schönstatt holy pictures, and handed them to Kreutzberg. 'I won't be needing these,' he said. 'Not where I'm going.'

'Would you sign these for me?' Kreutzberg asked. 'It could give some bit of joy to your friends at Schönstatt.'

Franz took the three little leaflets and wrote on the back of each – *Lieben u. leiden in Freuden.*[46] Then he added, to Kreutzberg: 'But don't you try to make a saint out of me!'

There was a pause. 'There's one other letter I'd like you to keep,' Franz said. 'You know that thing about the Pallottines expelling me? For refusing the oath?'

'I certainly do,' Kreutzberg muttered. 'And I think it's the most disgraceful and cowardly thing I ever heard. How could they have even have been so crass?'

Franz slowly unfolded a letter. 'I wrote this a good while ago,' he said. 'To my Provincial and his staff. It's dated 14 April, actually. They'd have received it back then, and acted on it. This is a copy, of course.' He handed it to Kreutzberg –

Dear Father Provincial

I believe you are already aware that I intend to refuse military service, and the oath to Adolf Hitler. You are also aware of my reasons for this.

In view of the fact that my stance could be harmful to my brethren in the Pallottines, and also to Schönstatt –

---

[46] Love and suffer in joy

through guilt by association – I write now to suggest that I be formally expelled from the Pallottine Congregation, and that you issue a decree to that effect, communicating the same to the Nazi authorities.

I should like to request, however, that I be allowed to remain a member *in pectore* [in secret], as both the Congregation and Schönstatt are everything to me.

I am taking the step of refusing the oath and military service because my conscience allows me no other option. I ask your prayers, and those of all the province, that God and Mary will give me the strength to endure what is to come.

Your brother in Christ

—*Franz Reinisch*

Kreutzberg silently folded the letter and put it in his briefcase along with the pictures and the breviary.

Every footstep in the corridor made them look to the door. But no one seemed to be coming.

'You know something, Heinrich.' Franz broke the silence. 'A thought keeps coming to me that I'll offer my life not just for the conversion of sinners, but also for saints. It's not just enough to care for conversions. We need many more holy people to come into the priesthood and into the laity of the church.'

'Will you remember me, Franzl, when – when you're up there?'

'I will keep my hand over you. And the Mother of God will guard you. And if you have a problem, just turn to me.' A smile. 'I'll already be rattling around God's throne!'

'Franz, you have a great grace: one could almost envy you.'

'Well, let me tell you, *you* have brought me great grace. Every wonderful word you spoke to me over these past days, I have construed as a word of Mary. Do you know something – if I'd known we'd have as much time as this, I'd have written a letter home.'

'Dictate one now. I'll use the shorthand.' He pulled out his notebook.

Franz put hands together and thought for a moment. Kreutzberg took down his words:

Dear parents

First a heartfelt God-bless-you for the last parcel and letter.
Dear Papa! You have no notion how much strength and power your end-of-June letter gave me. God bless you for it. And you too, dear Mother. With a little phrase, Franzl stay strong, you gave me a really great joy.

So I want to part from you with great blessings.

Your thankful *Franz.*

'And would you take this down as a message to the youngsters of Schönstatt? Just tell them, this:

Save your personality. Follow the voice of God in your breast. Follow your conscience. For by that God will judge

262

your life. Only people in conscience and responsibility before God can master the time and rescue the world.

'That's it. But wait, let's do another letter. I'd like to dictate one to Michael Kolb, you know the –'

'Reinisch! It's time. Come!' A jailer was at the door.

'Courage, Franzl. All courage and trust in God. We remain together –'

A sign of caution from Franz.

'– in prayer.'

A last handshake, and Franz left the cell with his jailer. Kreutzberg stood by the cell door and watched them as far as the iron stairs. He could hear the jailer's boots clunking all the way down until finally the exit door clanged shut. He turned to take one last look at the empty cell.

He was never to see Franz Reinisch again.

38

A man's conscience and his judgment is
the same thing; and as the judgment,
so also the conscience,
may be erroneous
Thomas Hobbes

BERLIN: Brandenburg-Görden Prison, 12 August, 1942. 11 a.m. O God, not another bloody chaplain. Another set of arguments to come; more attempts to convince him of the error of his ways. Franz Reinisch was fed up to the back teeth of explaining his position and answering all the standard arguments. And this new fellow could hardly be a friend like Heinrich Kreutzberg had been.

However Pastor Albrecht Jochmann seemed OK. Short, bespectacled, fiftyish, he first explained that he was pastor of the local Trinity Church, and was only standing in for the regular chaplain who was on leave of absence. He then came straight to the point, just to get it over with, as he explained. 'Your grounds for refusing the oath, dear Brother?'

Not again. Franz wearily went over his reasons one more time, from his early misgivings about the regime to his conviction that his conscience forbade the oath to that regime.

Jochmann listened carefully. Finally he said, 'I'll tell you frankly, dear Brother – I believe your comportment is based on an erroneous judgment of conscience. But on the other hand I also believe that you have so often gone over the thing, and that so many priests and advocates and professionals from all sides have worked on you, that I certainly won't try once again to influence you. Rest assured of that.'

Franz breathed a sigh of relief.

'No, I won't try to influence you,' Jochmann went on. 'In fact I deeply respect you. We are all experiencing so much unscrupulousness and lack of conscience and character in these times, so it is a relief to see someone sticking by his conscience. As I said, I hold your decision to be mistaken, and your conscience to be erroneous, but I also believe that no one can do greater than to hold true to his conscience under all circumstances, even until death. For such loyalty God will surely give the crown of eternal life.'

Franz stood and took the man's hand. He was near to tears. 'I cannot thank you enough, Father, for your understanding. You have just helped me more than I can say.'

BERLIN: Brandenburg-Görden Prison, 13 August, 1942. 3 a.m. *Erroneous conscience.* Those two little words – seeds of doubt planted by Pastor Jochmann – had worked their magic.

When the pastor called the following afternoon he found Franz Reinisch in a quite desperate state of anxiety and depression.

'You've given me a sleepless night with your exposition,' Reinisch told him. 'What you said about an erroneous conscience has not let me any rest. I've been going over it and over it and I can think of nothing else. Oh my God, what if my conscience *is* in error? Then I'm completely wrong in everything I've said and done. Oh, Father, what scandal have I given? What doubts have I sown? What hurt? I don't want to be obstinate, Father. I know that many clergy think other than I do. And yet, as often as I check the state of my conscience, I can come to no other judgment.

'But what if I'm *wrong?*' Franz put his head in his hands and it was clear he was weeping. 'And yet, I can never as a Christian take an oath of loyalty to a man like Hitler. Think what this man has done to the Church and to Germany, and to our Jews. And to Austria. But if I'm wrong? But my conscience is all I have. To make a vow to such a man, I cannot do.'

'Think of our Divine Saviour,' Jochmann said gently. 'Could he approve of the politics of the Romans, that insatiable imperialistic politics, that shameless exploiting of so many provinces? Certainly not. Nevertheless he recognised the Roman authority, even in his own fatherland. Remember – *Render unto Caesar the things that are Caesar's?* Over and over again he recognised the Roman authority. Again when he said to Pilate, *You have no power over me unless it be given to you from above.* Those words of our Saviour clearly emphasise the authority of state rule.'

267

'But didn't John the Baptist rebuke Herod for his sin? And paid with his life.'

'He rebuked, certainly. But he didn't refuse to obey in lawful things. Only in evil things. Look, dear Brother, if a child has wicked parents, he must not steal even when the parents tell him to. But in everything that is right he must obey the parents. And so must we obey lawful authority in all that is right.'

Franz stood up and clapped his hands. 'I think, Father, you have just given me the answer. Yes, in everything that is right, I must obey. *But this oath is not right.* An oath to obey that man in all things – *all* things – including conquering, exploiting, murder and massacre. Never. *Never.*'

He turned to Jochmann and there was a brief flash of the old temper. 'You know, Pastor Jochmann, you nearly had me. Nearly had me with that erroneous conscience bit. A pretty good try. I thank you for it. Because now I really know.'

BERLIN: Brandenburg-Görden Prison, 14 August, 1942. 7 a.m. Franz Reinisch knelt in prayer, as he had done for several hours.

There came the thud of boots outside on the corridor – the usual morning inspection. A rattle of keys and the cell door swung open. A warder looked in: 'What the fuck do you think you're doing, Reinisch? That praying will get you nowhere! There's only one way out of here for you, and you know what it is. The whole fucking prison knows. The dogs in the street know. Sign that bloody scrap of paper. There's not a prisoner here wouldn't love to be in your shoes – you just don't know how bloody lucky you are. If you weren't so stupid.

'Of course there's another way out for you.' The warder grinned and ran a finger across his throat before slamming the door.

At the midday inspection another warder came into Franz's cell. His was a new face. 'So what are you?' he demanded.

'Catholic.'

'Your profession, goddammit.'

'Catholic priest.'

'Priest is it? Know something – You ought to be rushed naked through a field of stubble, and hung from a lamppost, and blown into the air with dynamite.'

BERLIN: Brandenburg-Görden Prison, 15 August, 1942. Letter from Pastor Jochmann to Councillor Franz Reinisch (Senior), Innsbruck, Austria –

Dear Councillor

I deeply regret to have to tell you that your son will be shortly executed here. It will most likely take place within the next week or so, although nothing is certain in these cases. You will sadly have to deal with the aftermath of the carrying out of the sentence. As you will certainly wish that your son should have a christian burial, I urgently advise you to send a request to the state prosecutor in Potsdam, that the body be released, so that you can bury it at your expense. Denote the cemetery to which the body will be interred.

If a transfer to Innsbruck is too dear, or if it is not possible according to the current provisions, please let me know, so that the body can be buried in the old cemetery of Brandenburg.

It might perhaps be advisable that the approval of the release be requested first of all by telegraph, and then again by letter, likewise to the prosecutor. For the sake of being sure I would send the same letter to the director of the Brandenburg prison, Brandenburg/Havel, Winterfeld-Allee.

As I have said, I take it that the carrying out of the sentence is only a few days away; however there is nothing certain to say about that. If you want the burial to be in Brandenburg, I would gladly be ready to arrange the details here with the directors of the cemetery.

In warmest participation.

Gez.   *A. Jochmann*

Justice is a temporary thing that must at last come to an end;
But the conscience is eternal and will never die
Martin Luther

POTSDAM: Magdeburg-Berlin autobahn, 20 August, 1942. 5.20 p.m. A silver Fiat Ardita 2.5 litre sports car races towards Berlin at 150 km/h, far in excess of the legal speed limit. Driver Johann Baptist Reichhart is under considerable stress: he has only just finished eight executions at Mageburg-Neustadt and must now get to Berlin's Brandenburg-Görden Prison by 7 p.m., to prepare for a series of executions early in the morning.

His duties will include lubricating and testing the *Fallbeil* (guillotine) to ensure its correct functioning; whetting the blade to razor sharpness; checking on the physique and demeanour of the death candidates (to ensure that any resistance can be dealt with); and briefing the two assistants on all aspects of their duties. He will then take a well-earned rest in a specially-furnished cell, from which a warder will call him to an early breakfast at 3 a.m.

The *Fallbeil* is the German version of the guillotine. The word means 'mechanical hatchet' or, more literally, 'fall axe' – the preferred term since a French word would be unacceptable. Constructed of metal, the Fallbeil is superbly functional, far superior to the wooden French original. For some years it competed throughout Germany with the more traditional block and axe, until the Führer ordered it to become the standard form of execution for common criminals. It is both accurate and fast, important when there are large numbers of executions to be processed.

Reichhart, on loan from the Bavarian prison service, is seriously overworked due to the exponential rise in the number of wartime executions, which occasions his constant need to get rapidly from one prison to another. He has even asked the Reich Ministry of Transport for exemption from the legal speed limit: this however has been refused. However he still breaks the limit as he has little option, due to the obligations of his office.

In the boot of the car is folded the de rigueur formal dress of the German executioner – black frock coat, white shirt with double cuffs and links; white waistcoat, white gloves, striped pants, bow tie, black silk top hat. This creates an air of solemnity as a death candidate's head is removed.

The custom goes back to 1870s Prussia, when the then executioner, former knacker Julius Krautz, introduced the new formal wear in an effort to give his trade a certain bourgeois respectability in keeping with the culture of the times. Known in German as *Frack,* the formal dress was first used when Prussia resumed executions after some years, and beheaded

272

the would-be assassin Max Hödel, giving rise to the popular ditty –

> In black frock-coat and white waistcoat
> Did Krautz young Hòdel amputate !

Reichhart in these Nazi times is earning good money because of the amount of work that comes his way. He often has to deal with assembly-line executions, which could be up to 32 per day in certain prisons. And, apart from his annual salary of 3,000 Reichmarks, he receives a bonus for each head removed. A downside of course is that his children are regularly mocked in school, with the taunt that 'your papa's a *Kopfabschneider*'.[47] This will later lead a son to suicide.

BERLIN: Brandenburg-Görden Prison, 20 August, 1942. It is 7.45 p.m. The cell door clangs open and two warders step in. 'Reinisch, strip!' one of them orders. 'And place your clothes on the floor.'

This is ominous and something tightens in Franz's chest. He well knows that, when execution is near, there is always the danger that the condemned might attempt suicide – and an item of clothing could often serve as a rope.

He slowly removes his top and the loose trousers. Underpants are next.

'You can keep those,' the warder says. 'And the sandals, too. Now your hands, c'mon.' Shackles are placed on the wrists. 'And now, follow me.'

---

[47] Literally, 'head lopper' or 'head hacker'

Franz leaves the cell with a warder on either side, and shivers in the cold as they go down the long echoing stairs to the ground floor of the prison. Then to another set of stairs, leading to a basement. A miasma of excrement hangs in the air. There, on a couple of benches, sit six half-naked men, each in handcuffs and with a warder beside him. Franz and a guard move to the end of one of the benches.

Punctually at 8 p.m. the door swings open and a group of officials step in. Franz recognises the prosecutor from his trial, along with the prison doctor. Among the others are Pastor Jochmann, and another man in the attire of an evangelical chaplain.

The state prosecutor steps forward and produces a long, legal-looking document from a briefcase. His face has that sad but comfortable look of one who is not going to be executed. 'It is my duty first to inform you,' he says, 'that all pleas for mercy have been rejected, and the sentences will be carried out by beheading in the early hours of tomorrow morning. I will now read the sentence of death.' He clears his throat, opens the document and proceeds to read:

DECREE

On arrangement with the Upper State Agency of Potsdam, on Friday, the 21.8.1942, in the local institution, will the following death sentences be carried out at the times stated below:

4.50 a.m. Former gunner Bernhard Grimm, on account of Subversion of the Military Force – Jehovah Witness

4.53 a.m. Former Sergeant Friedrich Mennecke, on account of Treason – Catholic

4.56 a.m. Former soldier Franz Reinisch, on account of Subversion of the Military Force – Catholic

4.59 a.m. Former sergeant Arthur Müller, on account of Heavy Continued Embezzlement – Evangelical

5.05 a.m. Former rifleman Georg Schmalenbach, on account of Desertion and Other Things – Catholic

5.08 a.m. Former rifleman Horst Schumann, on account of Desertion etc – Evangelical

5.11 a.m. Former rifleman Fritz Glücks, on account of Desertion – Catholic

The bodies of the condemned – except for that of Reinisch, because of a special provision – will be handed over to the police administration of Brandenburg.

Brandenburg (Havel)-Görden
19 August 1942.
The Directors of the Prison and the Security Institution
In representation of the above:
Gez. *Dr THÜMMLER*
Government Councillor

The prosecutor finishes the reading, folds the document and places it back in the briefcase. He takes out a handkerchief to wipe his forehead, and turns to one of the officials. 'Now, I think the men should have something to eat and smoke. And they can write farewell letters to their relatives. Will you see they get paper and pencils? And you can take off the chains now.'

The warders turn to their charges to remove the handcuffs.

'And give them back their clothes. There's just been a change of rules.'

Then the prosecutor calls down the room: 'Reinisch, so you're going to your death, according to your wish. You know what your options are, don't you? But we're wasting our time with you.'

He then turns to an official and says quietly: 'You heard in the sentence that there's a special provision for Reinisch's body? The father to get it, and all that? Well, that's not going to happen. He's such a fanatical enemy of the state, we don't want any fancy funerals. He'll be burnt with the rest of them. There's a telegram going to the father to tell him that.' He raises his voice. 'All right then. You can take them off to the cells now.'

BERLIN: Brandenburg-Görden Prison, 20 August, 1942. 9.30 p.m. The basement holding cells are primitive and tiny – straw mattress on the floor, no blanket (could be used for suicide attempt), a chair, and a bucket in the corner. Understandable, for the denizens will not be there for long.

Each of the condemned has a warder to watch him. Franz finds himself with the warder who had yelled at him a few nights earlier – 'Praying is no bloody use.' Franz gives him the chair, and takes the mattress for himself.

The man seems gentler now, quieter. Perhaps it is the closeness of impending death. Or something in the prisoner's demeanour. Anyhow, Franz asks him what he had meant by that remark about praying being no use.

'To tell you the truth,' the man says, 'we're all up the walls by the stand you're taking. We'd love to see you freed – you've no idea of the effect you've had on us all. All this conscience thing – people are starting to think for themselves. It's all over the place. And the top brass know it. That's why they can't wait to see you go. One way or the other.'

10.05 p.m. Pastor Jochmann comes in. According to the rules, the warder then has to leave. Franz would like to have had more time with him.

'You have no more doubts, dear Brother?' Jochmann asks.

'None whatsoever.'

'Then, Brother, neither have I. I am completely and totally with you, in body and in spirit. Let us make this a night of prayer.'

Which is what they do. Pastor Jochmann has brought his Breviary – his book of daily prayer – and together they recite the Matins and Lauds for the coming day. The words from Psalm 142 resonate for both the men:

> In the morning let me know your love
> For I put my trust in you.
> Make me know the way I should walk
> To you I lift up my soul...
> Teach me to do your will,
> For you, O Lord, are my God.
> Let your good spirit guide me
> In ways that are level and smooth

And then they read from the Feast of the Assumption, for they are still within the octave of that feast: *Hodie Maria virgo caelos ascendit* – 'Today the Virgin Mary ascended to Heaven – rejoice.'

And Franz murmurs: 'Let me be there soon.' And then a quiet chuckle: 'Now, just think, in a few hours I will meet St. Peter, the first pope!'

12.15 a.m. Pastor Jochmann leaves, as he has to visit the three other condemned men who are Catholic.

Franz calls after him as he leaves: 'Will you visit Bernhard Grimm if they allow you, and salute him for me? He's a Jehovah Witness, and they're the only group who refuse the oath. You see, I'm not alone in this.'

Franz then sits on the straw mattress to write a last letter to his parents:

> Dear parents!
>
> ...I am only leaving you in body, and for that reason will once again thank you from my sincerest heart, for what you have been to me, as the greatest benefactors on earth.
>
> Mother, heartfelt thanks again for your packet. It was a foretaste of heavenly bliss.
>
> And Papa, in your last letter what you said about Jesus and Mary brought me really great consolation. And in a few short hours I will behold them all.
>
> I was sorry to hear from you that poor Anton Loidl has been killed in action. But I feel that I will meet him too up there.
>
> I am near you and remain so. For heaven and earth are not far distant from one another.

We have indeed heaven here on earth, if we live in the grace of God.For that reason I want you to be joyful when you hold this letter in your hand.

Then know: I am happy forever.

Your loving son

~ *Franzl*

1.45 a.m. Pastor Jochmann returns. Franz has been preparing for his last confession, and now kneels to make it. Among the things he confesses are his short temper and his impatience with others, weaknesses with which he has struggled all his life.

The pastor opens his little gilt box of hosts and gives Franz his last communion – the Viaticum for the dying.

2 a.m. The dull booming of the prison clock calls the hour.

'You know what I'm thinking,' Franz says. 'I'm thinking of the Curé of Ars on his deathbed. 'Do you know what he said? He said, "It's so sad to take communion for the last time".'

3 a.m. As the prison clock announces the hour, a warder enters. He is the same one who had talked with Franz earlier. 'I'm afraid, Father,' he said, 'I have to ask you to hand over anything you still have. You can put them in this bag, and we'll see that the Pastor here gets them – after you've gone.'

Franz hands over his last belongings – a handkerchief (the one in which he had wrapped the Communion hosts); his rosary beads; paper, pencil, and the farewell letter to his parents.

3.30 a.m. Last preparations for the execution. Franz has to take off his shoes and put on loose sandals. He has to remove his jacket. His arms are pulled back and he feels the handcuffs click into place. Then the jacket is put back on his shoulders, as the basement area is cold. The sleeves are left hanging loose.

A small procession, Franz, Jochmann and two warders leave the cell, cross the floor of the basement, and up the metal stairs to an annex on ground level. As in the basement area, there is a row of benches, with the other six condemned men already there, each with a warder on either side. One of the men is sobbing quietly. Another is vomiting into a bucket, but not quietly. The stench is powerful.

Again Franz finds himself at the end of one of the benches. On the opposite wall three steps lead to a door, behind which presumably is the execution chamber. Jochmann gives Franz a reassuring pat on the shoulder, leaves him, goes up the steps and through the door. There is a brief glimpse of lighted candles. The door clicks shut.

4.50 a.m. The name Bernhard Grimm is called. A handsome young fellow in his 20s stands, and two warders lead him up the steps and through the door.

4.53 a.m. The name Friedrich Mennecke is called.

4.56 a.m. 'Franz Reinisch!' The two warders lead Franz up the steps and through the door. A sweetish butcher-shop smell touches his nostrils. The room is like a small barn, painted dull green, with a corrugated iron roof. A black curtain runs across the room from wall to wall.

In front of the curtain stands the executioner, a tall man in *Frack* outfit – full formal dress, black frock coat, bow tie, white gloves, tall silk hat. The effect is somewhat spoiled by the bloodstained brown leather butcher's apron across his middle. There are also bloodstains on the white gloves. Two men, also in black, but not in formal dress, stand on either side of him.

In the centre of the room is a small table with a cross and two candles. Rather like an altar, Franz thinks, and then is mildly surprised that his mind is working so clearly. And that he is feeling no fear, but rather a kind of numbness. He just keeps repeating quietly, 'My Jesus, mercy; Mary help.'

At the left on the table is a legal-size pad with some writing on it.

Behind the table stand the Public Prosecutor, a magistrate, two official witnesses, on the left a doctor, and Pastor Jochmann on the right, holding a small silver crucifix. Franz is placed in front of the table, with a warder on either side.

'State your name,' the prosecutor says. He is the same man as before.

'Franz Dionysius Reinisch, Catholic priest.'

'Identify the prisoner.'

'This is Franz Reinisch,' one of the warders says.

The prosecutor then reads out the sentence of death. It is a slightly briefer version than that of the previous day.

There is a pause. Then the prosecutor says: 'Franz Reinisch, I am required to ask you, one final time, if you are ready to sign the *Fahneneid* – the Oath of Allegiance. If you do so, this execution will not take place. The paper is there on the table. Just put your name to it. That's all you have to do.'

'I thank you for your kindness,' the priest replies. 'But I cannot serve in an unjust war nor swear allegiance to an evil government. I die for Christ the King and for the Fatherland. May God bless you all.'

The prosecutor nods acceptance. Then: *'Scharfrichter, walten Sie ihres Amtes!'* [48]

The black curtain divides in the centre and silently slides back. Behind it stands the *Fallbeil* – the guillotine. Franz is surprised that it is not as high as he would have thought. The butcher-shop smell is stronger now.

Pastor Jochmann steps forward and holds the crucifix for him to kiss. The two assistant executioners come around to Franz, as the warders step aside. Taking him lightly by the arms, they lead him through the curtain to the guillotine.

'You want to face up or down?' the executioner asks.

'Down, please.'

'Step up here.'

Franz stands on a step facing a vertical metal stretcher. It is cold to the touch. He feels straps tighten around his back and legs. The stretcher is then tilted to horizontal, to click into place with the neck in a curved groove. A rectangular metal holding bar, also with a curved groove, is clamped above the neck. Franz looks down into a metal container full of blood-soaked sawdust. The smell of blood mingles with the sawdust smell.

He keeps whispering 'My Jesus, mercy. Mary help. My—|

They say there is no pain. The swiftness and razor-sharpness of the blade would indicate there probably isn't. But nobody knows for sure.

---

[48] Executioner, do your duty!

The executioner steps back into the room, doffs his top hat and bows. *'Das Urteil ist vollstreckt,'* [49] he announces.

INNSBRUCK, Austria. 22 August, 1942. When Pallottine member Father Johannes Tick, an old friend, called to the Reinisch family to bring them the news of the execution, he found that they already knew. The court had telegraphed the news.

Mother Reinisch made the visitor at ease: 'Dear Father, neither I nor my husband want to hear condolences. We are proud of our Franzl.'

When Tick told Papa Reinisch that his son, right up to the last moment, could have given a *JA* to the Oath and saved his life, but had refused, the papa's words were, 'Well, isn't our Franzl truly a hero!' And, as the three sat down to the evening meal, the papa said to his guest: 'So Father, now I'm going to the cellar – the best bottle of Tyrolean wine must today bear witness to that!'

Two days after the execution of Franz Reinisch, German troops reached the Volga. Then followed Stalingrad, and the beginning of the end for Nazi Germany.

THE END

---

[49] The sentence has been carried out

Source books

Reinisch, Franz. *Tagebuch aus dem Gefängnis. Märtyrer der Gewissenstreue*: Band 1 – *Im Angesicht des Todes.*. Vallendar: Schönstatt Verlag, 1987

Brantzen, Klaus. *Pater Franz Reinisch, Märtyrer der Gewissenstreue*: Band 2 – *Geheimnis der gekreuzigten Liebe.* Vallendar: Schönstatt Verlag, 1987

Brantzen, Emge & Hagmann. *Pater Franz Reinisch, Märtyrer der Gewissenstreue:* Band 3 – *Geht hinaus in alle Welt!* Vallendar: Schönstatt Verlag, 1993

Widerstand aus dem Glauben. Documentation – Pater Franz Reinisch SAC. Friedberg: Provinzialat der süddeutschen Pallottinerprovinz, 1993

Brantzen, Klaus. *Pater Franz Reinisch: Sein Lebensbild – Ein Mann steht zu seinem Gewissen.* Vallendar: Schönstatt Verlag, 1992

Kreutzberg. Heinrich. *Franz Reinisch: Ein Märtyrer unserer Zeit.* Limburg: Lahn-Verlag, 1952

Monnerjahn, Engelbert. *Schönstatt: Eine Einführung.* Schönstatt Verlag, 1993

Niederschlag, Heribert. *Prophetischer Protest: Der Entscheidungsweg von P. Franz Reinisch.* Vallendar: Patris Verlag, 2003

Feldmann, Christian. *Einen Eid auf Hitler? NIE.* Vallendar: Patris Verlag, 2012

Kordas, Wojciech. *Mut zum Widerstand: Die Verweigerung des Fahneneids von P. Franz Reinisch.* St Ottilien: EOS Verlag, 2002

Herman, Stewart W. *It's Your Souls We Want.* London: Hodder & Stoughton, 1943

Monnerjahn, Engelbert. *A Provocative Figure: Father Joseph Kentenich, Founder of Schönstatt.* Vallendar: Father Kentenich Secretariat, 1985

Anonymous.[50] *The Persecution of the Catholic Church in the Third Reich.* Gretna, LA: Pelican Publishing Company, 2003

Floyd, Wayne. *The Wisdom and Witness of Dietrich Bonhoeffer.* Minneapolis: Fortress Press, 2000

Delaforce, Patrick. *Adolf Hitler: The Curious and Macabre Anecdotes.* London: Fonthill Media, 2012

Evans, Richard J. *Rituals of Retribution: Capital Punishment in Germany, 1600-1987.* London: Penguin, 1996

Goldhagen, Daniel Jonah. *A Moral Reckoning.* New York: Vintage Books, 2003

Nasgorski, Andrew. *Hitlerland.* New York: Simon & Schuster, 2012

Rees, Laurence. *The Nazis: A Warning from History.* London: BBC Books, 2005

Goldhagen, Daniel Jonah. *Hitler's Willing Executioners: Ordinary Germans & the Holocaust.* London: Abacus, 1997

Fallada, Hans. *Alone in Berlin.* London: Penguin Classics, 2009

Rees, Laurence. *Their Darkest Hour.* London: Ebury Press, 2008

Bullock, Alan. *Hitler: A Study in Tyranny.* London: HarperCollins, 1991

Shirer, William L. *The Rise & Fall of the Third Reich.* New York: Simon & Schuster, 1990

Höhne, Heinz. *The Order of the Death's Head: The Story of Hitler's SS.* London: Penguin Classic, 2000

Gollwitzer, Kuhn & Schneider. *Dying We Live: Letters Written by Prisoners in Germany on the Eve of Execution.* London: Fontana, 1974

Steinhoff, Pechel & Showalter. *Voices from the Third Reich: An Oral History.* London: Grafton Books, 1991

Uriburu, Esteban. *A Father to Many: The Life & Work of Father Kentenich.* Vallendar: Patris Verlag, 1988

---

[50] Written in German, but published in translation in London (1940) and the United States (1942). The anonymous author is now thought to be Johann Neuhäusler, a priest later imprisoned in Dachau

Monnerjahn, Engelbert. *Joseph Kentenich: A Life for the Church.* Cape Town: Schoenstatt Publications, 1975

Wilenski, Gabriel. *Six Million Crucifixions: How Christian Teaching about Jews Paved the Road to the Holocaust.* San Diego: Qwerty Publishers, 2010

Lewy, Guenter. *The Catholic Church and Nazi Germany.* New York: McGraw-Hill, 1964

Pick, Daniel. *The Pursuit of the Nazi Mind.* Oxford University Press, 2012

Steinhoff, Pechel & Showalter. *Voices from the Third Reich.* London: Grafton Books, 1991

Rossi, Lauren Faulkner. *Wehrmacht Priests: Catholicism & the Nazi War of Annihilation.* Cambridge, Mass: Harvard University Press, 2015

Hanley, Boniface, OFM. *The Last Human Face: Franz Stock - A Priest in Hitler's Army.* West Milford, NJ: Self published, 2010

Whittock, Martyn. *The Third Reich: The Rise & Fall of the Nazis.* London: Constable & Robinson, 2011

Levi, Primo. *If this is a Man.* London: Orion Press, 1959

Owen, James. *Nuremberg: Evil on Trial.* London: Headline Review, 2007

Watkins, Olga. *A Greater Love.* Droxford: Splendid Books, 2011

Fest, Joachim. *Not I: Memoirs of a German Childhood.* London: Atlantic Books, 2012

Sereny, Gitta. *Albert Speer: His Battle with truth.* NewYork: Alfred Knopf, 1995

Floyd, Wayne Whitson. The Wisdom and Witness of Dietrich Bonhoeffer. Minneapolis: Fortress Press, 2000

Praise for books by David Rice

The Dragon's Brood

(HarperCollins)

David Rice's *Dragon's Brood* is a marvellously fresh and
immediate evocation ... He has a good journalist's sense of the
core of a human character, and a gift for asking questions...
His book achieves real depth. The belief that the Chinese care
little about individual or human rights... should not survive
these pages. Rice's eye is sharp and he has useful things to say
about many important topics.

—Mark Elvin in the London Review of Books

Illuminating recorded conversations... with explorations of
young people's views on all the issues which have been at the
forefront of change. Rice's view of China is not a cheerful one...
yet he maintains a justifiable spark of optimism.

—Colina Macdougall in The Times Literary Supplement

David Rice makes worthwhile reading... He accurately conveys
the often touching despair of most Chinese surveying the
wasteland of their recent past. He cleverly invokes their
alternating pride in China's size and cultural heritage and their
own sense of inferiority towards richer and freer westerners.

—Jasper Becker in The Times (London)

Where Jung Chang leaves off, David Rice takes over.

—Simon Scott Plummer in The Tablet

This intriguing book opens a wide window on the future which
before long we will all have to meet and greet and mingle with...
fundamental impression of truthfulness... my respect for an
enjoyable, enlightening and important book.

—Tony Parker in The Sunday Times

David Rice has done a commendable job in capturing the spirit of the times.

—John Kohut in the South China
Morning Post (Hong Kong)

I trust this book, because of what it says about Chinese faces.... Rice is a keen observer.

—Jonathan Mirsky in The Irish Times

The Dragon's Brood is a singular review of the thoughts and aspirations of a new generation of a people the West has too often misunderstood at its peril.

—Howard Rose in the Sunday Press

Song of Tiananmen Square

(Brandon/Mount Eagle)

Rice has written a gripping and all-too-realistic novel about the Tiananmen Square massacre and the events surrounding it.

—Chris Patten, last Governor of Hong Kong

Utterly fascinating... powerfully affecting... lyricism and immediacy.

—Robert Farren in The Irish Times

David Rice has recreated the sights, sounds, smells and, above all, the emotions of Beijing in the spring of 1989.

—Jonathan Mirsky, who reported the Tiananmen
Square massacre for The Observer

Shattered Vows

(Michael Joseph/Penguin; William Morrow NY; Blackstaff; Triumph Books; Ligouri Press)

Despite the anguish it portrays, *Shattered Vows* is an immensely heartening and encouraging book.

—Robert Nowell in The Sunday Times

Well documented and at the same time an outcry for changing the present disastrous policy.

—*Professor Hans Küng*

The unmistakable force and vividness that only real life can yield... The fruits of this patient listening are pictures we can see, and voices that speak to us.

—*Professor Uta Ranke-Heinemann,*
University of Essen, author of Nein und Amen

A call for candour on celibacy.

—*The New York Times*

This courageous exposé... provides powerful testimony. David Rice cannot be commended enough for his brilliant study.

—*Carol J. Lichtenberg in the Library Journal (US)*

I know no study... that compares with this. No one has researched the subject as well as David Rice. No one has listened... with such wisdom and sympathy.

—*Peter deRosa, author of Rebels;*
Vicars of Christ & others

His book has the convincing ring of truth... conveys an authentic impression... a very sensitive appraisal.

—*Dr Joyce M Bennett in the*
Church of England Newspaper

This book starkly says the Church is in crisis. Its author is well placed to know.

—*Michael Brown in the Yorkshire Post*

Kirche Ohne Priester

(C. Bertelsmann; Goldmann Verlag: German translation of
Shattered Vows*)*

A book without hate or rancour and an important contribution to the celibacy discussion.

—*Kronen Zeitung*

Rice has established a well-founded scrutiny of the present situation.

—*Braunschweiger Zeitung*

The Pompeii Syndrome / La Sindrome di Pompei

(Mercier Press) (also translation from Newton Compton, Rome)

The Pompeii Syndrome really grabbed me from the first page... it makes you wonder whether we really are in denial about catastrophic threat, because we refuse to believe in the possibility of our own extinction. My test of a good book is always the same - would I loan it to a friend with the proviso that they have to give it back? This definitely meets that criterion.

—*Brenda Power in The Sunday Times*

The Pompeii Syndrome is a genuinely terrifying, totally believable novel, because it could come true tomorrow ... What sets the story apart is the huge amount of research which underpins every paragraph. Rice has spent years studying the situation. He tells us - as the politicians never do - exactly what we can expect if we do not force our governments to change their policies before it is too late. Run, do not walk, to the nearest bookshop and buy a copy. Better still, buy copies for your friends as well.

—*Morgan Llywelyn, author of The Greener Shore; Grania; Red Branch & others*

A taut thriller... scarily believable. *The Pompeii Syndrome* is fastpaced and explosive... page-turning and thoughtful – a must-read thriller.

—*Cathy Kelly, author of Lessons in Heartbreak; Past Secrets & others*

Read this book or regret it till your dying day – which could be very soon...

—*Paul Williams, author of Evil Empire;*
The General (book & film), Gangland;
Crime Lords & others

Brilliantly narrated ... this is no ordinary novel, but 'fiction based on fact'... graphically portrays one route to mass destruction and the end of civilization as we know it. The 'Pompeii Syndrome'... may well enter the vocabulary alongside terms such as 'Stockholm Syndrome'. It refers to... denial in the face of impending catastrophe too awful to contemplate.

—*Louis Hughes OP in Spirituality magazine*

An absolutely gripping read.

—*Paul Carson, author of Scalpel;*
Cold Steel; Betrayal & others

The unthinkable becomes obvious. The moment when the obvious turns into reality, it is too late. And yet nothing changes. David Rice is the first one to put into words what many see coming but no one wants to see. Of course not. It would mean that something has to change. Now.

—*Mycle Schneider, international nuclear consultant, advisor to the official UK Committee on Radioactive Waste Management (CoRWM), and former advisor to the Belgian, French and German governments; winner of the 1997 Right Livelihood Award*

The Rathmines Stylebook

(Folens)

We are writing to be understood, and this book will help. Keep what you write simple and short and you can't go wrong.... When in doubt, refer to *The Rathmines Stylebook*.

—*Douglas Gageby, Editor, The Irish Times*

Blood Guilt

(Blackstaff Press)

One of the best-timed releases in modern publishing. David Rice had no idea that in the very week of its publication the central question posed by the book would be on the lips of thousands... What becomes of a gunman when his killing days are over?

—*Evening Press*

The great strength of this novel is that it is in no way mawkish and escapes the sentimentality so many people associated with the 'struggle'. The central character is sufficiently authentic to have the reader identify with his personal odyssey. *Blood Guilt* is an insightful, imaginative and well-crafted novel... Highly recommended, especially for those who appreciate the difference between style and pretension

—*Connacht Tribune*

#

More books you may enjoy from RED 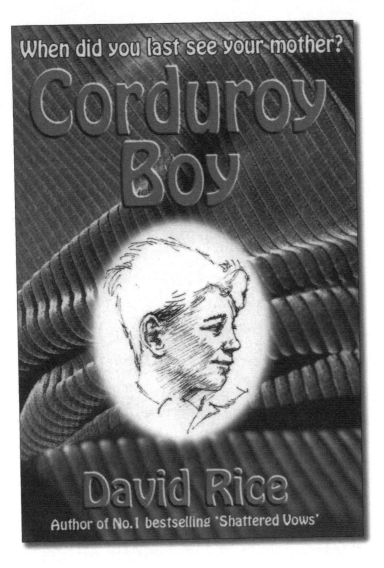 STAG (a Mentor imprint)

CORDUROY BOY

Corduroy Boy is a coming-of-age novel in which a scrupulous and deeply
troubled Catholic boy grows gradually to manhood and maturity, mentored by a dedicated teacher,
while both his family and his elite boarding school lurch towards terminal decline.

'A middle-class *Angela's Ashes*' – Gemma Mawdsley

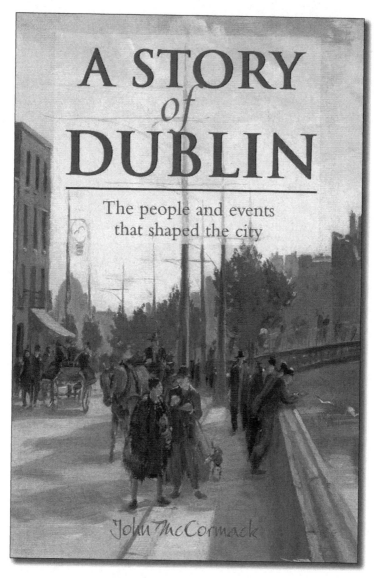

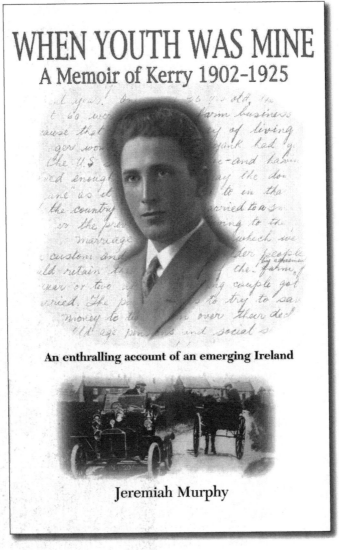

More books you may enjoy from RED  STAG (a Mentor imprint)

YOU TOO CAN DRAW

Do you ever wish you could draw a PORTRAIT, a LANDSCAPE, or even a STRAIGHT LINE?
Now YOU can do all this AND MUCH MORE when you follow the practical guidelines in this
invaluable book, illustrated with over 800 drawings. As the artist in you emerges, you will begin to see
everything in a new and creative way.

From leading bookshops or Mentor Books (www.mentorbooks.ie)
RED STAG (Mentor Books) ▪ 43 Furze Road ▪ Sandyford Industrial Estate ▪ Dublin 18
Tel: (01) 295 2112/3 ▪ Fax: (01) 295 2114 ▪ Email: admin@mentorbooks.ie